Gottfried Wilhelm Leibniz's General Investigations Concerning the Analysis of Concepts and Truths

A Translation and an Evaluation

UNIVERSITY OF GEORGIA MONOGRAPHS, NO. 17

Gottfried Wilhelm Leibniz's General Investigations Concerning the Analysis of Concepts and Truths

A Translation and an Evaluation

By
WALTER H. O'BRIANT
DEPARTMENT OF PHILOSOPHY AND RELIGION
UNIVERSITY OF GEORGIA

UNIVERSITY OF GEORGIA PRESS
ATHENS   1968

Copyright © 1968 by
University of Georgia Press

Library of Congress Catalog Card Number: 68-54890

Printed in the United States of America

Contents

Acknowledgments

THis work would not have been possible without the aid of a number of persons. Foremost among them is Professor Leroy E. Loemker of Emory University, who introduced me to the philosophy of Leibniz and later suggested to me the need for a translation and evaluation of Leibniz's *General Investigations*. His counsel concerning sources and his knowledge of the many facets of Leibniz's thought and era have been of great value. Under his criticism, the translation has become much more polished than I initially thought would be possible.

Acknowledgment must also be made to several other students of Leibniz's thought whose work has contributed quite substantially to my own. I have relied to a large extent upon M. Louis Couturat's edition of the text, although the rendering into German by Franz Schmidt has also been consulted. The treatment of the logical content of *General Investigations* by Raili Kauppi and Nicholas Rescher along with the earlier discussion by Couturat has been quite helpful.

Thanks are due Mr. David Estes of the Emory University Library, Mr. Herbert Hucks, Jr., of the Wofford College Library, and Mrs. Christine Burroughs of The University of Georgia Library for their help in securing materials, and to Mrs. Flora D. Colton of the University of Pennsylvania Library for comparing certain passages from Couturat's text with a microfilm copy of the manuscript in Leibniz's own hand.

Mrs. Sybil T. Bridges is due special thanks for the prompt and careful way in which she typed the translation.

Finally, I gratefully acknowledge my appreciation to my family who helped provide an atmosphere of encouragement and quiet in which to work.

W. H. O'Briant

Athens, Georgia

Introduction

An exact dating for Leibniz's composition of *General Investigations Concerning the Analysis of Concepts and Truths* cannot be established since the title and the date 1686 appear to have been added later.[1] Almost surely the final corrections and additions were completed by that date, but just how demanding of his time and energy this work was cannot now be known. Changes in pen and ink indicate that Leibniz was occupied with these investigations during at least three relatively distinct periods,[2] and the numerous changes indicate that he may well have returned to this manuscript again and again, sometimes after a brief respite and sometimes after longer intervals.

General Investigations is written on twelve sheets which constitute twenty-four pages (20 recto through 31 verso) in folio. About a quarter of the way through page 22 recto, Leibniz begins to affix numerals at the beginning of various sections—apparently as aids for reference. There is no consistent method for assigning these numerals. Sometimes they are assigned to a single statement; sometimes to several paragraphs. Generally, however, a change in the topic under consideration results in the assignment of a new numeral.

The manuscript is perhaps best characterized as a memorandum, or rather a group of memoranda, which Leibniz put down for his own benefit and which deals with logic—especially in relation to methodology and through it to epistemology and metaphysics. The tone of this work is tentative for the most part, as if Leibniz were putting down what came to his mind without always deciding what his final position on the matter would be. He never edited the manuscript for publication. Thus the manuscript contains a great deal of

1

repetition on certain points (sometimes with slight, but significant, changes), and is replete with additions and deletions along with often long marginal notes.

General Investigations remained in the Hanover Landesbibliothek (formerly *Königliche Öffentliche Bibliothek zu Hannover*) unpublished and apparently almost entirely unknown until M. Louis Couturat discovered it and published it as a part of his edited selection of Leibniz's writings on logic and related areas in *Opuscules et fragments inédits de Leibniz* (Paris: 1903).[3]

Since the manuscript is in Latin, it has until recently remained rather inaccessible to those interested in Leibniz's logic and related areas. However, in 1960 *General Investigations* appeared in a German translation with several explanatory notes by Franz Schmidt, and in 1966 it appeared in an English translation with introductory essay by G. H. R. Parkinson.[4] The present translation differs from the Couturat, Schmidt, and Parkinson editions in several respects. The most notable difference is the attempt to provide both reference notes to other Leibniz manuscripts (as Couturat mainly does) whenever they are helpful and explanatory notes for the text at hand (as Schmidt occasionally does and as Parkinson attempts in his "Introduction"), along with some treatment of the significance of *General Investigations* for Leibniz's other logical work and related areas of his philosophy.

The amount of attention which *General Investigations* has received is partial indication of its significance for Leibniz scholarship.

(a) It was first discussed by Couturat as part of his great work *La logique de Leibniz* (Paris: 1901). For him, the significance of *General Investigations* lies about entirely in the logic formulated in the manuscript. Couturat believes that in this work Leibniz discovered "the true and definitive translation of the four classic propositions into the algebra of logic, [the translation] which is the clearest, most symmetrical, and most suitable for the calculi."[5] Leibniz's dissatisfaction with this "simple and elegant notation" (because, e. g., it does not uphold traditional relations such as subalternation), and his preference for an intensional interpretation of his logic are unfortunate in Couturat's opinion because Couturat believes they prevented the establishment of Leibniz's logic upon the proper basis.

If he had been less attached to the scholastic tradition, he would have had less respect for these modes of erroneous reasoning, and the algebra of logic would have been constituted two centuries earlier upon definitive and solid bases.

Algorithmic logic cannot be founded upon intensional considerations. [Leibniz] needed to rely exclusively upon extension-which alone is susceptible of mathematical treatment.[6]

But perhaps the finest discovery in *General Investigations* is "the perfect analogy of categorical propositions and hypothetical propositions, [and] . . . of incomplex terms and complex terms, *i. e.*, of concepts and of propositions."[7]

Finally, Couturat contends, *General Investigations* "completes admirably the *Discourse on Metaphysics* and contains the logical foundations of it."[8] This is a particular instance of Couturat's more general claim that "the metaphysics of Leibniz rests uniquely upon the principles of his logic and everything proceeds from it in its entirety,"[9] and that Leibniz's logic is "not only the heart and soul of his system but the center of his intellectual activity and the source of all his inventions."[10]

(b) Bertrand Russell partially concurs in this claim. In the preface to the new edition of his *A Critical Exposition of the Philosophy of Leibniz*, written after he had seen Couturat's work, Russell states, "No candid reader of the 'Opuscules' can doubt that Leibniz's metaphysics was derived by him from the subject-predicate logic."[11]

(c) *General Investigations* was next treated in 1938 as part of Heinz L. Matzat's study of the metaphysical foundations of Leibniz's theory of symbols.[12] Matzat's treatment is little more than a paraphrase of Leibniz's own words (although occasionally he does attempt to amplify Leibniz's own statements by referring to other aspects of his thought), and is almost completely limited to the initial portion of the manuscript (prior to the numbered sections). However, in this connection Matzat does advance a theory about the relation between Leibniz's logic and metaphysics. His position is that, from the standpoint of the natural representation of the universe in the soul, the most primitive entities are construed metaphysically as monads, while from the standpoint of the artificial representation of the universe they must be construed as "first elements of the logical calculus."[13] He thus takes exception to Couturat's position.

The proposition originates as the true symbolic construction of substances which are represented monadologically. According to Leibniz, the proposition is thus not a logical given-ness from which the monadological metaphysics is derived, but it is rather . . . first of all conceived as a symbolic construction adapted for the essential relation of ideas to their foundation, the creative thinking of God.[14]

(d) The following year Matzat's efforts were attacked by Heinrich Scholz, who opened his review by asserting that he could not discover the meaning of the very statement which he took to be the basis of Matzat's investigation,[15] and closed by saying that Matzat was so conspicuously unfamiliar with the relevant material and so lacking in his command of mathematics and the Leibnizian theory of symbols that "such an instance ought not be repeated."[16] Scholz set forth in 1942 the results of his study of Leibniz's investigations into the foundations of mathematics, and concluded that, while Leibniz was unable to say everything that could be said in 1942, he did find all the fundamental assumptions necessary for the formulation of a *characteristic* and compares favorably with Frege.[17] Because of the disruptions accompanying World War II, this study was not widely disseminated.

(e) Then, in 1954, Nicholas Rescher published an article in which he re-examined Leibniz's logic with the explicit aim of undoing "some of the damage which Couturat's precon- ception [that the shortcomings of Leibniz's logic were due to his intensional approach] has done to the just understanding of Leibniz's logic and to the proper evaluation of his con- tribution."[18]

Rescher finds in Leibniz's mature[19] logical writings suf- ficient foreshadowings of the logistic treatment of formal logic for us properly to regard Leibniz as the father of symbolic logic. There is, according to Rescher, a common basis for all these efforts. It consists in the following features:

1. Variables whose range is a set of otherwise unspecified objects called "terms" (*termini*).

2. Singularly and binary operators on "terms" yielding "terms."
3. Binary relations between "terms," including equality.
4. The rules of inference[20] : i. Equality obtains between "term"-denoting complexes iff (if and only if) they are inter-substitutable in asserted statements.[21] ii. In any asserted statement involving some "term"-variable, this may be replaced throughout by another "term"—variable, or by some other "term"—denoting complex, and the result will again be an asserted statement. iii. The *modus ponens* rule. [If p, then q; p; therefore, q.]
5. A group of asserted statements which provides the axiomatic basis for the system.[22]

Leibniz constructed three main versions of his logical calculus, according to Rescher, and they can be distinguished from one another not only by means of certain peculiarities such as the use of small or capital letters, but also by the date of their formulation. This dating corresponds to that of Couturat: 1679, 1686, 1690.

General Investigations belongs to the second period, and Rescher regards it as "the main vehicle for the presentation of [Leibniz's second] system."[23] Moreover, according to Rescher, this is the same period during which Leibniz's metaphysical system assumed its final and completed form in almost every detail. This is no mere coincidence since Rescher believes that the system contained in *General Investigations* plays a central role in Leibniz's solution of a logical problem on which he felt the progress of his metaphysics to depend: the problem of reconciling his belief that there are true, contingent propositions with his conviction that all true propositions are analytic.[24]

And this, in Rescher's view, accounts for Leibniz's comment in the margin of *General Investigations*: "Herein I have made extraordinary progress."[25]

To Rescher, the second system is an extension of the first system, with changes such as the use of capital letters instead of small letters for symbols, and the introduction of "*ens*" ("being") or "*res*" ("thing") as a "term"-constant. Both systems have both intensional and extensional interpretations, and both accommodate the classical theory of immediate inference and of the syllogism.[26]

Rescher also finds in the second system a third interpretation which foreshadows C. I. Lewis's systems of strict implication. While on the intensional interpretation "terms" are properties, and on the extensional interpretation they are classes, on this third interpretation "terms" are propositions, *non* represents negation, juxtaposition represents conjunction, and *est* stands for the relation of entailment. *Ens* then represents logical necessity or logical truth. In Rescher's view, on this interpretation this system becomes a modal logic, and so Leibniz is a precursor of Lewis.[27]

Leibniz's third system Rescher calls "an improved extension of the first system."[28] But he does not make it clear just what the relation is between the second and third systems. Presumably, *General Investigations* made some contribution toward shaping the later system. Rescher conjectures that the "motivating force" for the development of the system of 1690 was Leibniz's "growing conviction that the notions of part, whole, and containment are the fundamental concepts of logic."[29] This system, then, is an axiomatic theory of containment, and Rescher seems to imply that *General Investigations* helped to nurture this conviction.

On the basis of this survey of Leibniz's logic, Rescher concludes that there is no support for Couturat's claim that "Leibniz's favoritism toward an intensional point of view had dire consequences for his logic."[30]

(f) In 1960, Raili Kauppi dealt with *General Investigations* in the course of a substantial volume on Leibniz's logic,[31] which goes well beyond previous studies and disagrees in part with Rescher's claims.

Kauppi agrees with Couturat that *General Investigations* contains the logical foundations for *Discourse on Metaphysics*,[32] and maintains that in *General Investigations* Leibniz is attempting not only to give a specimen of the logical calculus, but also to develop (at least in outline) the calculus from its simplest propositions and to exhibit its foundations. *General Investigations* was initially an investigation of truth in general[33] and therefore was to contain a calculus of contingent truths as well, according to Kauppi, but the concept of demonstrability within the context of the calculus was finally limited to reduction to identities, and this applies only in the case of necessary truths.[34] The analysis of all truth (which is possible only for God) forms then merely the metaphysical background which illuminates the wider relationships of the calculus.[35] With regard to *General Investigations* as actually developed, Kauppi asserts that "one of the leading ideas . . . is to show that the logic of propositions and of terms is the same," although they are distinguished by the fact that a term and its negation can be true (possible) at the same time, while a proposition and its negation cannot be true at the same time.[36] A second aim of Leibniz is "to derive the results of traditional logic from his logical calculus."[37]

In order to achieve this latter aim the traditional forms of the proposition have to be expressed by means of the calculus and then the various derivations carried out. Kauppi sees many attempts in *General Investigations* to find an adequate translation for the propositions, but believes that they fall into four main kinds of attempts: (1) The first[38] is not fully developed and consists in taking "A is B" as a universal affirmative proposition and representing the particular affirmative proposition by "AY is B." Universal negative propositions and particular negative propositions are expressed as negations of particular affirmative propositions and universal affirmative propositions, respectively. This yields:

UA: A is B UN: AY is not B
PA: AY is B PN: A is not B

Leibniz also represents these propositions by equations:

UA: $A = AB$ UN: $AY \neq AYB$
PA: $AY = AYB$ PN: $A \neq AB$

(2) Because of the inadequacy of this first attempt[39] Leibniz tries to represent propositions by negative terms.[40] Universal negative propositions are represented by universal affirmative propositions with a negative predicate. Since universal propositions are expressed as equalities, particular propositions are expressed as negations of these equalities:

UA: $A = AB$ UN: A = A non-B
PA: $A \neq$ A-non-B PN: $A \neq AB$

This representational scheme is vitiated by Leibniz's interpretation of "non-B" as what all things which do not contain B have in common, instead of regarding it as everything incompatible with B. This interpretation of negation as privation is not compatible with the demands of the calculus. (3) Leibniz is concerned that all terms be understood as possible, and in order to express that a term is possible he introduces a scheme using the expression "is" or "is a thing":[41]

UA: A non-B is not a thing   UN: AB is not a thing
PA: AB is a thing   PN: A non-B is a thing

In 1690 he introduces a similar scheme using the expression "being":

UA: A non-B is non-being   UN: AB is non-being
PA: AB is a being   PN: A non-B is being

On this scheme "A is not a being" coincides with "A is non-being." Since "non-being" originally involved pure privation, this change of signification means that now negation is distinguished from privation. This calculus in which the expressions "being" and "non-being" appear can be regarded as a modal calculus which considers only possibility and impossibility. Thus, Rescher is in error in identifying "being" with necessity, for the formulas have a meaningful interpretation only under the stipulation that "non-being" is understood as a contradiction. (4) Leibniz outlines the calculus of possibility in two different ways. According to the first scheme, an identity is true only if the terms are possible. Thus, "A = A" is equivalent to "A is being"; "A ≠ A," to "A is non-being." The formulas in "(3)" above are equivalent to the following:[42]

UA: A non-B ≠ A non-B   UN: AB ≠ AB
PA: AB = AB   PN: A non-B = A non-B

On this basis, from "A = A" one can conclude that every term contained in A is possible; from "A ≠ A," that every term which contains A is a contradiction. According to the second scheme, which Leibniz seems often to prefer, "A = A" is universally valid and the calculus of possibility forms a special case of the universal calculus in which terms can be formed without restriction. On this interpretation, "A is B" and "A is non-B" can be true at the same time when A is a contradiction, although in this case nothing useful can be concluded from "A = A."[43] In this calculus, hypotheses asserting the possibility of the terms must be introduced.[44]

Kauppi finds the viewpoint of *General Investigations* purely intensional.[45] Kauppi also points out, much more carefully than either Couturat or Rescher, what he believes are the main inadequacies of Leibniz's logic. Among these are: (1) the attempt to reduce all relations to that of inclusion, (2) the failure to develop fully a modal logic, especially the neglect of the modalities other than possibility and necessity, (3) the failure to carry through in the logical calculus the distinction between necessary and contingent truths, (4) the continual difficulties with the calculatory handling of negation (although Leibniz does come gradually to distinguish negation from privation explicitly), (5) the focusing of attention upon syntactical problems to the neglect of semantical issues such as denotation (symbol reference), and (6) the inability to construct a logic adequate for his metaphysics.[46]

(g) Finally, in a quite recent study of Leibniz's logic and metaphysics,[47] G. H. R. Parkinson disputes two of Couturat's central claims, *viz.*, that Leibniz preferred an intensional interpretation of his logic out of excessive respect for Aristotle, and that Leibniz's metaphysics is entirely derived from his logic.

Parkinson asserts that, while Leibniz mentions his agreement with Aristotle,[48] this is not at all the same as accepting a particular position *because* Aristotle held it, and that, if this were the only reason for Leibniz's choice, it would be no credit to him. Rather, Parkinson says, Leibniz had another and much better reason, *viz.*, that "concepts do not depend upon the existence of individuals."[49] Parkinson takes this to mean that it was Leibniz's desire to deny existential import to universal propositions which made him adopt the intensional approach. To refute "the commonly held view that Leibniz ascribed existential import to universal propositions," Parkinson cites a passage from *Difficultates quaedam Logicae*[50] where Leibniz resolves the problem of attributing existential import to universal propositions by denying it of particular propositions.[51]

The position of Couturat and Russell on the relation between Leibniz's logic and metaphysics is also denied. At the end of his discussion of the nature of the proposition according to Leibniz, Parkinson concludes:

It has not been seen that [Leibniz's logical] theory has of itself any consequences which relate to metaphysics, in the sense that it entails propositions which state what the world must be like, if there is a world. It is clear, then, that if Leibniz's logic has any consequences relating to metaphysics, these must be derived from a part of his logic which is other than that which has just been studied.[52]

His position is that Leibniz's logic must be regarded as only one source of his metaphysical assertions, and that "only a few propositions relating to metaphysics are, or can be, validly derived from his logic."[53]

Nevertheless, despite these studies, there is no general agreement about the significance of *General Investigations*. As the above survey indicates, assessments of the work are not only varied, they are often incompatible.

No doubt there is much about this manuscript which can only have been understood by Leibniz, but there are aspects about which a meaningful assessment can be made, and until there is clarity about these matters there can be no overall evaluation of *General Investigations*. One of the main tasks of the present work, then, will be to clarify the nature of the manuscript and to arrive at an evaluation in relation not only to Leibniz's logic, but also to his methodology, epistemology, and metaphysics. This will be accomplished through an introductory essay, a translation of the text into English, and a critical commentary upon the text.

THE ROLE OF *General Investigations* IN THE DEVELOPMENT OF LEIBNIZ'S LOGIC

Leibniz believed that it was possible to discover a number of simple concepts by means of which all other concepts could be expressed. Just how many simple concepts Leibniz envisaged is not clear. His treatment in the initial portion of *General Investigations* of what he there calls "simple primitive terms" suggests that the number is small. But Leibniz also believed that the simple concepts had their basis in the simple perfections of God, and this suggests there might be an infinite number of simple concepts. Perhaps Leibniz never reconciled these two positions in his own thinking. In any case, he held that by assigning a name or simple sign to each of these simple concepts "the alphabet of human thought" could be constructed. Knowledge of this alphabet and the various combinations of names or signs would be the means not only to all that is already known, but also to the discovery of new knowledge.[54] Thus, to aid in the art of invention or discovery (*art d'inventer*), there must be developed a combinatorial art (*ars combinatoria*) so that all the possible combinations of concepts and the relations between (or among) them can be determined.[55]

Out of this develops Leibniz's plan for a "universal characteristic" (*characteristica universalis*). According to this method, simple concepts would be replaced by their signs, complex concepts would be expressed by combinations of these signs, propositions would be expressed by the relations between or among signs, and reasoning would become a sort of mechanical procedure. Instead of saying, "Come, let us reason!" one would say, "Come, let us calculate!"[56] Thus the universal characteristic would provide a universal and infallible method for demonstrating truths and discovering new ones, for judging and discovering.[57]

From the dating of the manuscripts, Leibniz seems to have been most concerned with the problem of the formulation of the universal language itself around 1678. He did not claim to be the first to conceive of such a language since

for a long time excellent men have brought to light a kind of "universal language" or "characteristic" in which diverse concepts and things were to be brought together in an appropriate order. . . . However, nobody, so far, has gotten hold of a language which would embrace both the technique of discovering new propositions and their critical examination. . . .[58]

Leibniz believed that he knew the way to formulate such a language (*viz.*, by establishing characteristic numbers for concepts), and that "a few selected persons might be able to do the whole thing in five years."[59] His optimism was to prove unfounded, of course, for the task was not nearly so simple as he first conceived of it.

Now, in the broadest sense, Leibniz conceives of logic as the "art of thinking."[60] It is a method for ordering what is known, demonstrating from what is known, and discovering the yet unknown; and involves both analysis (the breaking down of concepts into their constitutent concepts) and synthesis (the putting together of concepts from these constitutent concepts).[61] Moreover, two types of logic can be distinguished: a logic of the certain, and a logic of the probable. The former makes use of the universal characteristic; the latter, the calculus of probabilities.[62]

But, in a narrower sense, Leibniz means by logic the logical calculus, and it is primarily as a contribution to the development of this calculus and its relations to other areas of his thought that *General Investigations* must be viewed, although *General Investigations* also considers problems such as the combining of concepts which are more properly part of the art of combinations.

Since one of the methodological assumptions of the project for a universal characteristic was that simple concepts could be represented by a single character and that a composite concept could be represented by a combination of characters, it is quite natural that in his initial attempts in 1679 to find the universal calculus which would facilitate the discovery of relations among characters, *etc.*, Leibniz maintains this same assumption.[63] Thus, Leibniz conceives of the analysis of concepts into simple elements as analogous to the analysis of numbers into prime factors, and the composition of concepts as analogous to arithmetical multiplication so that a composite concept is represented by the product of the prime numbers which stand for simple concepts. For example, "Man is a rational animal" could be represented by "$6 = 2 \times 3$." A concept then has as its predicates all the concepts represented by the prime factors and their multiplicative combinations found in the number representing the initial concept. Applied to propositions, this means that a universal affirmative proposition is true if the number representing the predicate is a factor of the number representing the subject, or "$S = Py$." The particular affirmative proposition is "$Sx = Py$." Then, taking negative propositions as the respective negations of affirmative propositions, the universal negative proposition is represented as "$Sx \neq Py$," and the particular negative proposition is represented as "$S \neq Py$."[64] But Leibniz finds these latter two translations unsatisfactory since all possible values of x and y would have to be tested in order to verify the values of the coefficients.[65]

Thus, Leibniz revises his method. First, he changes universal negative propositions to universal affirmative propositions with a negative predicate, and particular negative propositions to particular affirmative propositions with a negative predicate. Secondly, he decides to express negative terms as a function of affirmative terms with a minus sign, and to represent negative terms with negative numbers. On this basis a universal affirmative such as "Every sage is pious" is true, if "sage" is represented by "+70 −33" and pious by "+10 −3," since 70 is divisible by 10 and 33 by 3. But Leibniz is also led to give up this system because it becomes very inconvenient—if not impossible—to assign to each term two characteristic numbers which meet all the conditions of validity, and further this system does not always reveal invalidity.[66]

Leibniz now turns away temporarily from the attempt to assign characteristic numbers to concepts and begins to use letters along with the copula "is."[67] A universal affirmative proposition has the form "a is b." The commutative law and the law of tautology constitute two of the principles of this calculus, along with three axioms: the principle of identity ("a is a"), the principle of simplification ("ab is a" or "ab is b"), and the principle of the syllogism ("if a is b and b is c, a is c"). Identity of terms is established by the possibility of intersubstitution, and the relation between identity and inclusion is given: "if a is b and if b is a, a and b are identical." From this point, Leibniz goes on to establish laws regarding the analysis and synthesis of propositions. Several predicates of the same subject can be united into one: "if a is b, and a is c, a is bc," and inversely a composite predicate can be analyzed into its elements: "if a is bc, then a is b and a is c." But, while subjects of the same predicate can be compounded, they cannot be separated. Next Leibniz establishes the theorem that the terms of a proposition can be multiplied by the same factor, from which it follows that several propositions can be multiplied term by term so as to form one proposition which has the product of their subjects for its subject and the product of their predicates for its predicate. But the terms of a proposition cannot be divided by the same term, nor can a common factor be eliminated. Leibniz stipulates that one letter can be made the equivalent (by definition) of another letter or combination of letters, and that what is proved with regard to an arbitrarily selected letter will be valid for all letters which meet the conditions.[68]

There follows a period of almost complete inactivity in his logical works[69] which probably ends in late 1685 or early 1686. The most important manuscript of this second period of logical activity is *General Investigations*. *Prima facie* it differs from the earlier works in that, while small letters and the copula "is" are more often used in the earlier writings, capital letters and the copula of equality predominate in *General Investigations*.

However, the logical content of *General Investigations* is not vastly different from that of earlier works. Basic assumptions (*e. g.*, that the relation of containment is fundamental to understanding the connection between terms and between propositions) remain essentially unchanged as Leibniz directs his attention to questions concerning the relations between terms, categorical propositions, and hypothetical propositions; schemes for representing these relations diagrammatically and numerically; and the formulation of principles for a logical calculus. He does, of course, at first attempt to avoid merely stipulating certain symbols and rules for manipulating them by surveying the structure of the natural language Latin in the belief that *the* logic which he seeks will be found embedded therein; but when this fails he proceeds in somewhat the same way as he has before, *viz.*, representing composite concepts by the multiplication of simple concepts, sometimes using letters, sometimes numbers, sometimes the copula of equality, sometimes the copula of inclusion.[70] Leibniz's demands upon the logical calculi continue to be shaped largely in terms of a formulation of the four classical forms of propositions adequate for making explicit the immediate and mediate logical relations which he believes to hold between or among them (*e. g.*, conversion and superimplication).

Thus, Leibniz's efforts in *General Investigations* are reminiscent of his thinking concerning a logical calculus in 1679. Yet even if *General Investigations* were simply a summary of earlier work in logic it would be significant as a more coherent and rigorous treatment—although, of course, still not as coherent and rigorous as even Leibniz would wish. This must be at least a part of what Leibniz means in his note: "Herein I have made extraordinary progress."

Following the composition of *General Investigations* there is another pause in Leibniz's logical activity until 1690.

In two fragments from that year[71] Leibniz continues to make use of multiplication and the copula of equality. The initial method here is to reduce all propositions to affirmative or negative judgments of existence:

UA: A non-B = 0   UN: AB = 0
PA: AB ≠ 0   PN: A non-B ≠ 0

Using a second method the propositions are reduced to equalities:

UA: A = AB   UN: A = A non-B
PA: A ≠ A non-B   PN: A ≠ AB

He sees that the methods are equivalent and therefore demonstrates that (AB ≠ 0) = (A ≠ A non-B) and (AB = 0) = (A = A non-B). But Leibniz continues to have difficulties since he wishes to attribute existential import to particular propositions and also to allow logical procedures such as partial conversion. In a fragment which Erdmann has called *Difficultates Logicae*[72] Leibniz examines some of these difficulties—principally the one just mentioned. If partial conversion is allowed, the problem arises as to how existential import can be attributed to particular propositions but not to universals. Leibniz tries to remove this difficulty by attributing existential import to all propositions. But then he is faced with the question of whether a universal affirmative proposition is false if there is no actual instance of it at the moment. He tries to get around this by saying that "All A is B" means "If there are any A's, they are B's." But then it does not have existential import, and conversion is possible only if there is the added premise: "There is an A." And in fact Leibniz does add such a premise.[73]

Thus the methods used in these writings are essentially the same as those in *General Investigations*.

But one of the problems which continue to plague Leibniz is the problem of incommensurable fractions—the result of using multiplication to represent logical multiplication and division to represent negation.[74] So in a series of later writings[75] (though perhaps still belonging to the year 1690) Leibniz turns to a system of logic in which addition represents logical multiplication (*e. g.*, A + B = C) and the relation of logical equality is almost completely dominant. Thus, he moves beyond *General Investigations* as far as this aspect of the logical calculus is concerned. In this respect, it could be said that *General Investigations* represents the final major effort on Leibniz's part to develop his calculus by using multiplication.

But none of these later manuscripts deals with the range of related issues to be found in *General Investigations*. They are relatively fragmentary attempts to formulate the calculus in the sense of setting forth the primitive symbols and rules for manipulation. But there is no major effort to relate the logical problems to a wider range of issues in methodology, epistemology, metaphysics, and so on.

Thus *General Investigations* is significant not only for its logical content, but also because in it Leibniz grapples with the wider range of problems which he believed were raised by his logic. It would never have occurred to Leibniz to attempt to formulate a "logic without ontology." The way in which he persistently re-thinks the question of existential import, continually asking whether anything corresponding to such concepts or propositions must exist, is good evidence for this. No doubt this is in part the attitude which has led some commentators to hold that Leibniz's logic is the sole basis for his metaphysics.

The Relation of *General Investigations* to Leibniz's Methodology, Epistemology, and Metaphysics

Early in his thinking, Leibniz makes a distinction between necessary and contingent propositions. Such a distinction is explicit in *On Freedom* which dates from *c*. 1679, and is implicit in an even earlier work, *A New Method for Learning and Teaching Jurisprudence*, which dates from *c*. 1667 in its initial form.[76]

This differentiation involves rather fundamental, methodological assumptions. For Leibniz, methodological procedures fall into two types: analysis and synthesis. In analysis, a judgment is broken down into its component judgments or concepts (a judgment being ultimately an assertion about how concepts are related), or a complex concept is broken down into its simpler concepts. Such an analysis would lead at last, in Leibniz's view, to the "simple[st] concepts" (perhaps a very few). A perfect analysis always yields such concepts as its end product. Synthesis, in contrast, consists in putting together concepts or judgments so that they stand in the proper relations to one another. If the simplest concepts and the various possible proper combinations of such concepts were known, then by starting with what is known to be true, it would be feasible to extend our knowledge solely by the method of synthesis, by reason in contrast to sense experience. As has already been indicated, this is fundamental to the quest for a universal characteristic and a "calculus of reason."

Now analysis can assure us only of the possibility of a concept or a judgment, *i. e.*, that it is free of any logical contradiction. In the case of truths of reason, once their possibility is established we can be certain about their truth. But because of our human limitations, especially our inability to carry out an analysis involving an infinite number of steps, possibility cannot always be established solely on rational grounds. Therefore, we must turn to experience. If we can find an exemplification of a given concept or judgment, then we can be assured of its possibility since obviously what is actual must be possible also. Truths of fact then depend upon experience.

These considerations are evident in *On Freedom* as Leibniz is confronted with the problem of reconciling his belief in the contingency of things with the principle that every proposition (or at least every true affirmative proposition—universal, particular, or singular; necessary or contingent) is analytic, *i. e.*, the concept of the predicate is involved, explicitly or implicitly, in the concept of the subject. Leibniz starts from the position that all truth is either original or derivative. Original truths are those for which no reason can be assigned, *i. e.*, identities. Derivative truths are of two kinds: those which can be reduced to primary truths in a finite number of steps, and those which can be reduced only in an infinite number of steps—the former being necessary truths, the latter, contingent truths. Of course, the complete analysis of contingent truths cannot be accomplished by us. It can only be done by God. And such truths depend upon the intellect and will of God, since not every possibility achieves actuality and therefore a divine choice is involved.

In *General Investigations* Leibniz distinguishes between the two kinds of truth on basically the same grounds,[77] but he is less explicit about the dependence of contingent truths upon God's decrees[78] and he is unclear just how to relate this distinction to the distinction between true and false propositions. There is then no significant progress beyond the position taken in *On Freedom.*

In another treatise, *Discourse on Metaphysics,*[79] which dates from the same period as *General Investigations*, Leibniz introduces this distinction between necessary and contingent truths in connection with his discussion of the principle that the concept of an individual (in the sense of Leibniz's metaphysics) contains once and for all everything that has happened, is happening, and will happen to him.[80] To the assertion that this principle destroys the distinction between two kinds of truth, Leibniz replies that a distinction must be made between what is certain and what is necessary. Future contingents are certain since God foresees them, but they are not necessary. A proposition is absolutely necessary if its opposite implies a contradiction. A proposition whose opposite does not imply a contradiction is in itself contingent, although it may be necessary *ex hypothesi, i. e.,* given the free decrees of God.

Thus the distinction between two kinds of truths as made in *Discourse* is fundamentally the same as that in *On Freedom.*

However, in *New Essays Concerning Human Understanding*, which Leibniz seems to have completed around 1710, and which were finally published in 1765, he speaks of the distinction between the two kinds of truth in somewhat different terms.

Primitive truths, which are known by *intuition*, are of two kinds, like the derivative. They are truths of *reason* or truth of *fact*. Truths of reason are necessary, and those of fact are contingent. The primitive truths of reason are those which I call . . . *identical, . . .*

As for the *primitive truths of fact*, they are the immediate internal experiences of an *immediateness of feeling*. . . . [*E. g.*,] *I think* . . . All *primitive truths* of reason or of fact have this in common, that they cannot be proved by anything more certain.

[In addition to propositions of fact and propositions of reason] . . . there are . . . *mixed propositions*, drawn from premises, some of which come from facts and observations, and others are necessary propositions. . . . These mixed propositions have only the certainty and generality which belong to the observations. As for the *eternal truths*, it must be observed that at bottom they are *all* conditional and say in effect: such a thing posited, such another thing is. For example, . . . *every figure which has three sides will also have three angles.* . . .

In what is this connection founded[?] . . . It is in the connection of ideas. . . . This leads us finally to the ultimate ground of truths, viz.: to that Supreme and Universal Mind, which cannot fail to exist, whose understanding, to speak truly, is the region of eternal truths . . . These necessary truths contain the determining reason and the regulating principles of existences. . . .[81]

Though the language of this account is not entirely that of the earlier accounts, they are not irreconcilable. The failure to express the distinction in terms of finite analysis and infinite analysis is of no special significance since the distinction is not expressed in those terms even in *Discourse on Metaphysics*; furthermore, in these passages from *New Essays* Leibniz is talking about *primitive* truths of both kinds, and analysis is not applicable to them. It must also be recalled that in his earlier treatises Leibniz was making the distinction between kinds of truths from the standpoint of an irreducible dichotomy between divine knowledge and human knowledge. But in *New Essays* Leibniz is concerned primarily with *human* understanding. He is saying, in effect, "Granted our human limitations, this is how *in practice* the distinction between truths of fact and those of reason must be made, and sometimes they are mixed."

While this proposed reconciliation may have its difficulties, it has the distinctive advantage of giving continuity to Leibniz's thought.

The significance of *General Investigations* for more strictly metaphysical aspects of Leibniz's philosophy is found primarily in the consideration of two topics, *viz.*, the nature of the concept of an individual, and existence, possibility, and compossibility.

In the opening remarks of *General Investigations* Leibniz asserts that every term is accepted as "complete or substantive" and that no distinction is needed between adjective and substantive (except perhaps for emphasis).[82] Of course, if "substantive" and "complete" are equivalent as applied to terms, not every "complete term" represents an individual (in the metaphysical sense). For example, the word "sword" is logically complete, yet it does not denote one individual (in the sense of a metaphysical substance).[83] Rather it denotes a group or society of individuals—those monads which provide the foundation of a given sword.

Then, in section 71, Leibniz changes his position by admitting that some substantives are not complete. Thus, "Peter" is an individual or complete term, but "man" is an incomplete term because it does not involve everything that can properly be said of an individual man.[84] The criterion for distinguishing the concept of an individual from other concepts is the superfluousness of adding "some" or another concept to the concept of the individual (*e. g.*, "some Alexander the Great," "Alexander the Great the conqueror"). Complete concepts cannot form part of concepts more complex than themselves.[85]

As Leibniz says in section 8 of *Discourse on Metaphysics*:

It is the nature of an individual concept or complete being to have a concept so complete that it is sufficient to make us understand and deduce from it all the predicates of the subject to which the concept is attributed. An accident, on the other hand, is a being whose concept does not include everything which can be attributed to the subject to which the concept is attributed.

Thus, from the concept of the Apostle Peter there is deducible every predicate attributable to him, *e. g.*, that he denied three times and that he existed. But, of course, the perfect analysis of the concept of any individual requires an infinite number of steps, and so can be carried out only by God. Such truths of fact are beyond human capacity to establish. Indeed, Leibniz's position is even more confined since he is unable to show how even one of the attributes of an individual can be shown to follow from the concept of that individual.

This is especially unfortunate since among those attributes which it would be of signal importance to know whether a

given individual possessed is that of existence. "To exist" obviously means more than just "to be possible" since there are
possibilities which are never actualized. While logic can
establish what is possible by determining what does not involve a contradiction, it cannot itself establish what actually
exists. Leibniz's discussion of this issue in sections 71-74 of
General Investigations indicates that existence (or non-exist-
ence) follows not merely from the concept of a given individual, but from that concept in relation to the concepts of
other individuals as comprehended by a "most powerful mind."
A judgment is made not about just the possibility of certain
concepts, but about their *compossibility*, *i. e.*, their co-existence in a *uni*verse so as to achieve maximum fullness of content with minimum disorder. Obviously, this is not a purely
logical standard; the logical criterion is secondary to a theo-
logico-metaphysical criterion.[86]

As indicated earlier, *General Investigations* is particularly
significant since in no other treatise does Leibniz attempt so
persistently to treat his logic in relation to other areas of his
thought, especially metaphysics. Yet the attempt is ultimately
unsuccessful, since the metaphysical doctrines central to the
work are not supported by the logical doctrines or *vice
versa*. Indeed, such must be the case from the nature of his
metaphysics and logic.[87] Two considerations make this evident.

(a) In *General Investigations* Leibniz asserts, "Every
proposition as it is ordinarily expressed comes back to the
fact that it says which term contains which. . . ."[88] Thus, the
fundamental relation within the proposition is that of containment; the concept of the subject contains that of the predicate.[89]

In his metaphysical speculations (especially after 1690
when he is occupied with working out a dynamics) Leibniz
is concerned to take account of such features as change, continuity, and individuality. Leibniz holds that the universe consists of an infinite number of individuals, *viz.*, the monads,
each of which contains all its modifications and is harmonious-
ly related to all the others, but not causally influenced by
them. While the perfections of all other monads are based
upon the infinite perfections of the Supreme Monad, the
relation between Creator and creatures is not one of contain-

ment, for this would entail the existence of only one meta-physical individual and lead Leibniz straight to "Spinozism."

Now the propositions which are more important from the metaphysical standpoint are those which have the concepts of individuals (complete concepts) for their subjects, *i. e.*, singular propositions. Presumably an analysis of such a proposition would tell us whether a given individual possesses a given attribute, if such an analysis could be accomplished. Yet in his logic Leibniz deals almost exclusively with universal and particular propositions, which have *incomplete* concepts for their subjects. Indeed, he attempts to treat singular propositions as a special case of universal propositions,[90] perhaps thinking of a universal proposition such as "All men are mortal" as analyzable into the singular propositions "Socrates is mortal," "Plato is mortal," *etc.* But Leibniz never shows how, starting from the universal proposition, these singular propositions are derivable.

Thus, at this point, Leibniz's logic and metaphysics fail to support one another because each one concentrates on what is less important from the standpoint of the other. His metaphysics requires a true plurality of individuals, but the centrality of the notion of all finite perfections being derived from the infinite perfections of God seems to point ultimately to only one individual, God, who is explicitly or implicitly the logical subject of every proposition.

(b) Leibniz often asserts that "there are no purely extrinsic denominations."[91] Assuming "extrinsic denomination" to denote a relation, and "intrinsic denomination" to denote a predicate, this doctrine seems to require that all supposed relations be reducible to predicates. *E. g.*, all propositions stated in relational form should be statable as propositions of subject-predicate form.[92] In discussing the status of the ratio between two lines L and M, Leibniz says:

This relation . . . is indeed out of the subjects; but being neither a substance, nor an accident, it must be a mere ideal thing, the consideration of which is nevertheless useful.[93]

My judgment about relations is that paternity in David is one thing; sonship in Solomon another, but that the relation common to both is a merely mental thing whose basis is the modifications of the individuals.[94]

This indicates that for Leibniz relations are phenomenal, although there is a basis for them, *i. e.* they are "well-founded phenomena," in the mind of God.

From the viewpoint of his metaphysics, Leibniz looks upon a monad as containing implicitly all its states and thus as having its "windows" closed as far as causal relations are concerned. Statements about relations between monads are ultimately statements about the states of each monad. Again, relations are phenomenal, though not illusory.

Yet in neither his logic nor his metaphysics does Leibniz show how relations can be treated in the requisite manner. He never indicates how a logical relation such as "owner of" can be reduced to a predicative form. He sees that traditional logic cannot handle relational propositions, but he is unable to develop his own logic so that it is adequate in this respect. Nor does Leibniz make clear how relations can have the metaphysical status he assigns them. Ascribing them to the mind of God still leaves unanswered the question of whether they are reducible to attributes, qualities, *etc.*

So again the logic and the metaphysics fail mutually to support one another.

There is, indeed, a remarkable parallelism between certain logical and certain metaphysical principles. But instead of one set of principles entailing the other or their significantly supporting one another, there is a persistent ambiguity about their mutual status—an ambiguity which might be expected in the work of a thinker who could write: "My system . . . is not a complete body of philosophy. . . ."[95]

General Investigations AND THE DEVELOPMENT OF MODERN LOGIC

The logical expressions in *General Investigations* show that Leibniz achieved many of the insights central to modern logic as exemplified in formulations such as Boolean algebra and Whitehead and Russell's *Principia Mathematica*. He discovered that, if the principle that $AA = A$ were introduced, then propositions could be treated according to algebraic principles, and he gave algebraic translations of the four classical forms of propositions so that both variables and constants could be expressed symbolically and dealt with "mechanically," according to explicit principles. He knew the relation between the copula of equality and the copula of inclusion, and saw how hypothetical propositions could be treated analogously to categorical propositions containing the copula "is." He formulated the operations of logical multiplication, addition, and negation as well as laws such as identity and non-contradiction.

While he was aware of the problem of assigning existential import to propositions, Leibniz did not take a definitive position—largely because on the one hand he wished to retain the relations on the traditional square of opposition, while on the other hand he could not achieve symbolic formulations which justified such. In this respect, Leibniz must be looked upon as more of a traditionalist, since in general only the relation of contradiction survives in modern logic.

Although Couturat has labeled Leibniz as a traditionalist on the grounds that his preference for an intensional interpretation of his logic is the result of excessive respect for Aristotle,[96] the position is untenable. Of course, Leibniz does prefer an intensional interpretation. But this is because of his understanding of the nature of the proposition and his predilection for divine knowledge,[97] not just because Aristotle also held such a position.[98] Nor does this preference have the dire consequences which Couturat claimed.[99] Leibniz himself, of course, explicitly recognizes the possibility of an extensional interpretation.[100] And most of the inadequacies of his logic are due, not to an intensional interpretation as such, but to the limits of the task which he apparently set for himself, *viz.*, to accommodate the traditional logic of the concept, the proposition, and the syllogism within the framework of a universal language and explicitly stated rules of inference.

This vision of a logical language based upon explicitly stated assumptions, definitions, and rules of inference, and manipulated in a precise manner is modern. But Leibniz's efforts to realize this vision were guided in large measure by a more traditional way of thinking which thought largely in terms such as the subject-predicate characterization of propositions and the justification of relations such as subimplication.

Now, as was mentioned in the preceding, almost all of Leibniz's work in logic remained unpublished and largely unknown until the turn of this century when Couturat made some of it readily available. Thus, if one begins to trace the history of modern logic to its origins one finds that the credit for founding modern logic must go to Boole, Frege, Peano, and their contemporaries, not to Leibniz.[101] For they made their discoveries independently of Leibniz's detailed work in logic. Thus, while Leibniz may be called the inventor of symbolic and mathematical logic, he is not the father for he was without progeny.[102]

The question naturally arises: Why did not Leibniz himself publish his work in logic or in some other way communicate it to a wider audience? There is no simple answer to this question. Though he certainly believed that he had made some important discoveries, Leibniz never revised his logical works so as to make them suitable for publication. This is in part due to his many other interests and responsibilities as well as his failure to develop a single, coherent logical system. But there is no doubt another reason. His logic had failed to undergird his metaphysics as he had once hoped it would. And yet Leibniz believed that his metaphysics offered the best hope of achieving a social order which would make possible the "felicity of spirits." His logical studies were left behind as he went forward with his metaphysics. Finally, what if he had published? Who would have been his readers? He might have valued Arnauld's opinion of *Discourse on Metaphysics*, but the author of the Port-Royal Logic would hardly be receptive to Leibniz's logical work. Nor would the scholastics be a likely source of counsel. In brief, Leibniz was far enough beyond his contemporaries that he had no one for whom to publish.[103] And to this day his works have lacked the audience they undoubtedly deserve.

But even if Leibniz's logical work had been published, there would have remained a major hurdle to the formulation of a modern logic, *viz.*, the formulation of a logic adequate to deal with relations. For all his insight, Leibniz's logic is limited to propositions which can be handled on the subject-predicate basis. While he was certainly aware of relational propositions,[104] he failed in his attempt to handle them by reformulating them as subject-predicate propositions. Had Leibniz formulated a logic which could handle relations beyond those of inclusion and identity, he might have found also the logic demanded by his metaphysics.

Perhaps Leibniz would have discovered this if he had continued his work in logic. What he did see is enough to mark him off as one of the great logicians of all time.

EDITING OF THE TEXT: APPARATUS AND GENERAL POLICY

The translation which follows is based mainly upon Couturat's edition of the text in *LLL*, though the entire text has been compared with the translation in *Fragmente zur Logik*, trans. and ed. Franz Schmidt (Berlin: Akademie-Verlag, 1960), and certain passages have been compared with the microfilm on deposit at the Library of the University of Pennsylvania to insure accuracy. However, to keep the body of the text as uncluttered as possible, the additions and deletions which Leibniz indicated have been made without their being noted except in the case of changes of unusual significance. Also, several corrections have been incorporated into the text without noting them, since the errors were seemingly due to carelessness.

The punctuation of the Couturat edition has been kept unless the length or sense of the sentence in English called for a change. Italics indicate Leibniz's own underlining, but quotation marks have been added for clarity.

All of Couturat's notes which have been retained are followed by "(C.)."

Leibniz used a horizontal "8" for the sign of logical equality; this translation follows Couturat in replacing Leibniz's sign by "=."

Headings have been inserted into the manuscript by the translator to provide a sectional outline. They do not correspond to divisions by Leibniz except at sec. 136.

Bibliographical Reference Keys

LLL   Couturat, Louis. *La logique de Leibniz*. Paris, 1901.

Phil.   Leibniz, Gottfried Wilhelm. *Die philosophischen Schriften von Gottfried Wilhelm Leibniz*, hrsg. von C. I. Gerhardt. 7 vols., Berlin, 1875-90.

OF   ‥‥‥‥‥‥. *Opuscules et fragments inédits de Leibniz,*
        ed. Louis Couturat. Paris, 1903.

PPL   ‥‥‥‥‥‥ . *Philosophical Papers and Letters,* selected,
        trans., and ed. by Leroy E. Loemker. 2 vols.
        Chicago: Univ. of Chicago Press, 1956.

Symbols Used in the Text

*   An asterisk follows a word which is doubtful—usually
    due to illegibility.

[ ]   Brackets in the text enclose words or phrases which
    Leibniz indicated were to be deleted.

*12   A numeral preceded by an asterisk indicates the place
    at which the corresponding marginal note is to be in-
    serted. Since printed pages do not always correspond to
    manuscript pages, these marginal notes are placed at the
    bottom of the appropriate printed page.

General Investigations Concerning the Analysis of Concepts and Truths

1686

*1 AN ANALYSIS OF THE ELEMENTS OF LANGUAGE

(20 recto-20 verso)

FOR the present at least, we shall omit every-   [20 recto]
thing abstract so that all terms will be understood to apply
only to concretes, whether they be substances, like "I," or
phenomena, like the rainbow. Thus we shall not be concerned
now about the distinction between abstract and concrete, or
at least we shall not now consider abstractions except those
which are logical or conceptual; for example, the B-ness of A
signifies nothing other than that the A is B.

Non-A is *privative*. Non-non-A is the same as A.

A is positive if it is not any non-Y, and Y is similarly assumed not to be non-A, *etc*. Every term is understood to be
positive unless there is indication that it is privative. "Positive"
is the same as "being."

"Non-being" is what is purely privative, or privative of all
things, or non-Y; *i.e.*, non-A, non-B, non-C, *etc.*; and this is
what is popularly stated as: there are no properties of nothing.

Also we here accept every term as complete, or substantive, so that "great" is the same as "great being," or,
so to speak, "great one." Just as a big-nosed person is called
"Nose," so in these investigations we do not need a distinction
between adjective and substantive, except perhaps for indicating an emphasis.

Being is either *per se* or *per accidens*, or a term is either
necessary or changeable. Thus, man is being *per se*; but learned
man and king are beings *per accidens*. For that thing which is
called "man" cannot cease to be man, unless he be annihilated;
but one can begin or cease to be king or learned, although
he remains the same.

---

*¹Herein I have made extraordinary progress.

Either a term is *integral* or perfect, for example, "being," or "learned," or "the same as or similar to A"—namely, terms which can be the subject or the predicate of a proposition, although nothing is added—or it is *partial* or imperfect, for example, "same," "similar"—where something must be added (namely, "to A") in order to create an integral term. And in fact what must be added is joined to it obliquely; when being added to an integral, a direct term can always be added, or omitted, without impairing the integrity of the term. And two integral terms which constitute a new integral are connected *in recto*. But not every term to which another is added *in obliquo* is partial; thus "sword" is integral, although it be turned into "sword of Euander" by adding to it obliquely. Thus something non-direct can be omitted without impairing the integrity of the term, for example here, the oblique term "of Euander." But, on the other hand, an oblique term, when the direct term has been omitted, does not make an integral term. Therefore if a term integral *per se* be added with some inflection or mark of connection to another—with the result that by omitting the other it is not made an integral—it has been added in the oblique. However, an integral term can be made from an oblique term which has been disjoined from a direct term. For example, from the oblique term "of Euander" can be made "that which is a thing of Euander," or "Euandrian."

It will be useful, however, to see to it that the terms are integral. Furthermore, there is a need for certain general signs of things or terms; thus, if we are willing always to employ in our *characteristica* only integral terms, we ought not to say "Caesar is similar to Alexander," but "Caesar is similar to the A who is Alexander" or "similar to the thing which is Alexander." Thus our term will not be "similar," but "similar to the A." In the same way, we should not use the expression "sword of Euander," but we should say "sword which is the thing of Euander," so that "which is the thing of Euander" is one integral term. In this way we should be able to divide any composite term into integrals. To what extent and by what method we can carry this out, progress will tell, but if it goes on forever we shall have no other names than integrals. We shall see whether we can in a similar way form integrals *from particles*. For example, in place of "A in B," "A *existing in something* which is B."

Moreover, from these remarks it is evident that there are integrals which may be analyzed into partials, and that there are direct terms in which (if you were to analyze them or substitute the definition for the thing defined) oblique terms would clearly be elements. Partials therefore—and likewise particles which added to oblique terms make direct terms and added to partials make integrals—ought to be explained first rather than the integrals which are analyzed into partials and particles. Nevertheless, before explaining partials and particles, we ought to explain those integrals which either are not analyzed or are analyzed only into integers. And it is especially necessary that such integrals—at least the general ones like the term "being"—be independent of partials, for the partials themselves need these in order to pass over into integrals because the ultimate complement of a partial or an oblique term by means of which the latter passes over into an integral cannot be analyzed further into an integral and a partial since it is integral. We need an enumeration of such integrals which are, as far as we are concerned, unanalyzable into obliques and partials, and which an analysis of the remaining terms will give. It will suffice for a beginning to enumerate those as purely integral whose resolution into non-integrals seems less needed. The matter is thus to be reduced to this: that, given a few integrals composed of partials and obliques, all the rest may be compounded directly or similarly, *i.e.*, without obliques. In this way a small number of integrals—either defined with certainty or progressing in a definite series—which we should be able to consider as primitives could be established by a direct analysis, and from these the remaining more composite terms may then arise just as derivative numbers arise from primitives. By this method its own characteristic number may be assigned to any concept whatever in so far as it is analyzed without obliqueness.

Accordingly, we have: first, *simple primi-*   [20 verso] *tive integral terms* which are unanalyzable or assumed to be unanalyzable, like A *[2]; secondly, simple particles or primitive

---

[2]By "term" I understand an integral term, for partials are made from an integral and a particle, as for example a part is a "being in" another, *etc.*

syncategorematics, as "*in*"; thirdly, *primitive integral terms* compounded from purely simple terms, with the composition taking place directly or without intervention of particles or a syncategorematic, as *AB*. Fourthly, there are *particles compounded* from pure, simple particles without the intervention of a (categorematic) term, as "within"; we can use this particle for designating (if it then be added to syncategorematics) a thing which "*with*" something is "*in*" something. Fifthly, we have *simple derivative integral terms*. I call those terms *derivative* which do not originate through composition alone, *i.e.*, through similarity, or the composition of a direct term with a direct term, like AB; but which originate by the interposition of a certain flection or particle or by the interposition of a syncategorematic; as "A in B" where A and B enter in a dissimilar manner as constituents into a term compounded out of just these, namely, the "A in B." In a way the grammarians also observe this difference between composition and derivation. There are, therefore, simple derivative terms which are not analyzable into other derivatives, but only into simple primitives with particles. Sixthly, we have *composite derivative integral terms*, which naturally are composed *directly or similarly* from other derivatives, and these are also composed obliquely from primitives joined together with particles. Seventhly, it is debatable with regard to those *derivatives which are derived from simple primitives and composite particles* whether they are more simple than composite. Obviously, they are not analyzable into other categorematics except by the duplication of one primitive, since by joining it now with one now with another *simple* particle, forming a composite, we can make two new simple derivatives from which the posited derivative, as if composite, can be made. Eighthly, in the same way as we have derivative and primitive categorematic terms, so we also can have *derivative particles*, and these in turn can be simple particles derivative from a simple particle and a primitive term; or (ninthly) *composites* from a composite particle and a primitive term, which can be analyzed into a greater number of simple derivative particles. Tenthly, in a similar manner it is unclear what we should say about a particle derived from a composite primitive term and a simple particle. *³ Furthermore, we must also take into consideration the fact that even simple primitive particles are not joined in a manner similar to simple primitive terms. Therefore, there can be many variations in the composition of particles. As an example, if I say "John-of-Peter-of-Paul," *i.e.,* "John son of Peter who was son of Paul," there is a certain similar composition; but if I say "Socrates of Sophroniscus from Athens," there is a dissimilar composition of particles or of inflections. And from this no doubt diverse relationships will arise, both diverse obliquities and mixtures of obliquities, with whose careful arrangement the most important part of the *ars characteristica* is concerned. But no satisfactory judgment can be made concerning those until the simple primitives in terms as well as in particles are arranged with absolute exactness; or—at least for the present until a way naturally opens little by little for their further analysis—instead of those let us assume terms which are admittedly derivative and composite, but which are more nearly related to simple primitive terms. Under particles also I understand here some primitive partials, if they are such as cannot be analyzed into other primitive partials. But I think that in fact they are made from "being" or some other integral term with a particle.

Simple Primitive Terms (21 recto)

Let the following be *simple primitive terms,*   [21 recto] or terms to be accepted in the meantime as simple and primitive:

Term (by which I understand *being* as well as *non-being*). *Being* or possible (but here I understand always concrete terms, since I have excluded abstracts as unnecessary). *Existing* (although in fact a cause of existence can be assigned, and "existing" can be defined as "what is compatible with more things than any other thing which is incompatible with existing itself." Nevertheless we must abstain now from these loftier considerations.) *Individual* (Although all being in truth

---

*³Perhaps nevertheless it is better to leave all the particles, as well as all the obliques, just as we said on the preceding page—unless of course it is objected that it will not be so readily apparent which are to be related to which.

be individual, nevertheless we are defining only terms which designate either any individual of a certain given nature, or some certain determinate individual, as "man" or "any man" signifies any individual partaking of human nature. But *This* is a certain individual, which I designate either by pointing him out or by adding his distinguishing marks [Although in fact marks perfectly distinguishing one individual from every other possible individual cannot be given, still there are available marks distinguishing one individual from the other individuals encountered.].) *I* (There is something peculiar and hard to explain in this concept; yet, since it is an integral, I have thought that it ought to be placed here.)

Additional simple primitive terms are all those confused phenomena of the senses which we certainly perceive clearly, but which we cannot explain distinctly, neither define them through other concepts, nor designate them by words. Thus we are able to say many things to a blind man about extension, intension, figure, and other variations which accompany colors, but—beyond the accompanying distinct concepts—there is in the color something enigmatic which no blind man aided by any words of ours can conceive, unless at some time it be granted to him to open his eyes. And in this sense, "white," "red," "yellow," "azure," to whatever extent they consist in that inexplicable vividness of our imagination, are primitive terms. Nevertheless it will be useful, since they are enigmatic and add nothing to reasoning, to avoid them as far as it is permissible by employing the accompanying distinct concepts as definitions in so far as they sufficiently distinguish the enigmatic aspects from each other. Sometimes it will be useful also to mix the two methods with each other as far as it is suitable, and in this way we can give proper designations to those primaries, while the rest are explained by means of them. Thus "colored" is a term which may be explained through its relation to our eyes, but because this relation cannot be expressed accurately without many words, and because, in the second place, "eye" itself is in need of an extended explanation, just like some machine, we shall be able to assume "colored" as a simple primitive term, by which, when certain distinguishing marks are added, we shall be able to designate various colors. Nevertheless, perhaps "colored" will be definable by means of the perception of the surface without sensible contact. But which of these methods is preferable will become evident in the procedure.

It seems that among simple primitives can be numbered all the concepts which contain matter of a certain quantity, or in which homogeneous things accord with one another, as for example "having magnitude," "extended," "enduring," "intensity"; but these concepts—unless I am mistaken—so far cannot be analyzed. Concerning concepts of the extended and of thinking in particular it is problematical whether they are simple; in fact many judge that these are concepts which may be conceived *per se* and do not require further analysis. Yet the extended appears to be a continuum having co-existing parts. Also, the term "thinking" seems not to be integral, for there is reference to some object which is being thought. Nevertheless there is contained in thinking itself some absolute reality which is difficult to explain in words. And in extension we seem to conceive something other than continuity and existence. Nonetheless the concept of extension seems full enough so that we conceive a continuous co-existence such that all co-existents form a unity, and whatever exists in extension is continuable or repeatable without interruption. Meanwhile, if it seems to the point to take extension or even position (or existing in space) as a simple primitive, just as thinking too (either a one expressing many with immanent actions, or consciousness), there is no harm done, particularly if we then add certain axioms from which all other propositions are deduced by adding definitions. But all these matters, as I have often said, will be better made evident from the progress of the discussion itself. And it is preferable to proceed rather than to remain stuck at the very beginning by a certain excessive scrupulousness.

PARTIAL TERMS; THE RELATION OF COINCIDENCE; THE
DEFINITION OF "TRUE" AND "FALSE"; AND THE RELATION OF
CONTAINMENT (21 verso-24 recto, sec. 59)

Now let us try to explain *partial terms* or   [21 verso] relational ones from which particles indicating the relation of terms also originate. What comes to mind first as I make this inquiry is "*same.*" That A is the same as B signifies that

one can be substituted for the other in any proposition whatsoever without destroying its truth.*[4] Now those relations
are explained by means of propositions or truths. Thus "Alexander the Great" and "king of Macedonia, vanquisher of
Darius" can be substituted for one another, as also "triangular"
and "trilateral." Moreover, these can always be shown always
to coincide by an analysis, namely, if they are analyzed
until it appears *a priori* that they themselves are possible and
furthermore if the same terms formally result, then the diverse terms are really the same. Let A be a term and B be a
term; if the definition be substituted for one as well as the
other, and in turn the definition for any constituent, until
one comes to simple primitives, the result in one will be
what it is in the other or formally the same. Therefore A
and B will be *coincidents*, or virtually the same. So therefore
we can give the definition:

A coincides with B, if the one can be substituted for the
other without destroying its truth, or if, when both are
analyzed by the substitution of values (or definitions) for
terms, the results are the same on both sides—that is, formally
the same—for example, if on both sides the results were:
L.M.N. The changes which are made by substituting the definition for the thing defined, or conversely, occur without
destroying its truth. From this it follows: if A coincides with
B, B also coincides with A.

The next concept is that A is the *subject*, B the *predicate*,
if B can be substituted for A without destroying the truth, or
if, when A and B are analyzed, the results in B are results
also in A. This same thing can be explained in another way:
A is B, if *all* A and *some* B coincide.

Therefore we have the designations: *"coinciding* with
B itself," *"subject"* and *"predicate,"* *"is,"* *"all,"* *"some."*

If "Some A is B" is asserted, this means: "Some A and

---

*[4]We ought to see whether, when it is posited that A can be sub-
stituted in any place whatever for B, it also follows in turn that B can
be substituted in any place whatever for A; doubtless if those terms stand
in a similar, reciprocal relation with one another, then the substitution
is reciprocal. But if they do not stand in a similar relation, obviously
neither are they in the same mode to any third term nor will we then be
able to substitute one for the other.

some B coincide." From this it also follows: "Some B is A."

If all A and some B coincide, some A and some B also coincide. But still this seems demonstrable from negatives; therefore let us proceed to them.

As A and A are the first coincidents so A and non-A are the first *disparates*. There is a disparate, if it is false that some A is B. Thus if B = non-A, it is false that some A is B.

Generally if A is B, it is false that A is non-B.

If it is false that some A is non-B, one says, "No A is non-B," or "*All* A is B."

Hence these consequences will be demonstrable: "*All A is B*"; therefore, "*Some A is B*," i.e., all A and some B coincide. Therefore, some A and some B coincide. If all A and some B coincide, then it is false that some A and some non-B coincide (from the definition of *all*). Therefore it is true that some A and some B coincide.

But it is important to treat more accurately   [22 recto] the whole matter of propositions and the relations of terms which arise from various propositions. Here a source of many partial terms and particles is to be assumed.

*5

*6

*7

I say that propositions *coincide* if one can be substituted for the other without destroying its truth, or they are inferred reciprocally.

(1) These coincide: the (direct) proposition L and the (reflexive) proposition "L is true." Hence, "It is true that L is true (false)," and "Therefore L is true (false)" coincide. (Preferably, these should be differentiated according to propositions correctly ordered.) (Generally if A is a term, or if one can always say, "A is true," it coincides with a certain proposition.)

---

*5(Any letter such as A, B, L, *etc.*, signifies for me either some integral term or some entire proposition.)

*6(When one term stands for many terms, the latter are a definition or more explicit value; the former, the defined. For example, if I put C instead of AB, or when A = BC is a primitive proposition.)

*7(A and B coincide, if through substitution of more explicit values for the terms, and conversely, the same true (false) formula results on each of the two sides.)

⊙ These coincide: "L is true," and "It is *false* that L is false."

That it is true that L is false, and that L is false coincide. I can demonstrate this kind of a theorem in this manner: That L is false is a proposition which is called M. Now "M is true" and "M" coincide (by 1). Therefore by assigning the value for "M," "It is true that L is false" and "L is false" coincide.

(The same thing may be done in another way more generally by ⊙ also being applied. It is demonstrated in this way: it is true that L is false coincides with the proposition that it is false that it is false that L is false (by ⊙); and that in turn with the proposition that it is false that L is true (by the same ⊙); and finally with the proposition that L is false (by 1).)

(2) If A and B coincide, non-A and non-B also coincide. "A-non-A" is a *contradiction*.

Possible is what does not contain a contradiction or "A-non-A." Possible is what is not "Y-non-Y."

Non-non-A and A coincide, and so, if non-A and B coincide, non-B and A also will coincide.

(3) Non-true and false coincide.

Therefore also non-false and true will coincide.

If A = B, then non-A = non-B.

If A = some truth, then non-A = non-some truth or no truth or a falsehood, for non-A contains non-AY.

*8

(4) "It is true that L is true" and "It is non-true that L is non-true" coincide. Further, L and "It is false that L is false" coincide. L is the same as "L is true"; and this is the same as "It is true that L is true" (by 1); and this is the same as "It is not true that L is non-true" (by 4); and this is the same as "It is false that L is false" (by 3).

L and "It is non-false that L is non-false" coincide. L coincides with, is the same as, "It is true that L is true" (by 1), and this is the same as "It is non-false that L is non-false" (by 3).

---

*8All these things are intelligible if the terms are possible, for otherwise neither truth nor falsehood has a place in the propositions in which the terms are constituents.

That L is false and "It is non-false that L is non-true" coincide.

That L is false and "It is non-true that L is non-false" coincide. This is easily shown from the preceding.

In general, if a proposition be called "true" or "non-true," "false" or "non-false," then "true" times "true" or "false" times "false" makes "true." "Non" times "non" is equivalent to the omission of both.

Also from this it is demonstrated that every proposition is either true or false; or, if L is non-true, it is false. If it is true, it is non-false; if it is non-false, it is true; if it is false, it is non-true. All by 3.

Moreover, propositions 1, 2, 3, 4 serve as definitions, and therefore they are assumed without proof, for they indicate the use of certain signs, namely those of truth and falsity, of affirmation and negation.*[9]

A is B (either B is in A, or B can be substi-   [22 verso] tuted for A).

"A coincides with B," "A does not coincide with B" is a [categorical] *proposition.*

Here, A and B can signify terms or other propositions.

(5) "A does not coincide with B" is the same as "It is false that A coincides with B."

(6) If A coincides with B, B coincides with A.

(7) If A does not coincide with B, B does not coincide with A.

(8) If A coincides with B, and B coincides with C, then A coincides with C.

(9) If A coincides with B, non-A coincides with non-B.

These four axioms are corollaries of the definition that

---

*[9]I say that something is impossible or contains a contradiction if the term is an incomplex term containing A-non-A, or if it is a proposition which in turn either says that those of which one contains the contradictory of the other coincide, or itself contains an impossible, incomplex term; for whenever those of which the one contains the contradictory of the other are said to coincide, such an assertion always contains a contradictory term; whenever something contains that of which it contains the contradictory it always contains a contradictory term. And so when an impossible proposition is employed, an incomplex, contradictory term results.

those things coincide of which one can be substituted for the other.

(10) A *proposition true per se* is: "A coincides with A."

(11) A *proposition false per se* is: "A coincides with non-A."

(12) Thus we conclude that it is false that non-A coincides with A (by 6).

(13) Likewise we conclude that it is true that A does not coincide with non-A (by 5).

These propositions can be counted among the propositions true *per consequentiam*.

Moreover A—as I have said here—signifies a term or a proposition. Hence non-A signifies the contradictory of a term or the contradictory of a proposition.

(14) If a proposition be posited, and nothing is added to it, it is considered to be true. This coincides with 1.

(15) "Non-B coincides with non-B" is a corollary of 10, if it is posited that non-B coincides with A.

(16) An *affirmative proposition*: "A is B" or "A contains B," or (as Aristotle says) "B is in A" (namely, *in recto*), *i.e.*, if a value be substituted for A the result will be: "A coincides with BY." For example, "Man is an animal" or "Man is the same as . . . animal," *i.e.*, "Man is the same as rational animal." By the mark "Y" I signify something indefinite, as "BY" is the same as "some B" or ". . . animal" (where "rational" is understood, if only we know what is to be understood) or "some animal." Thus "A is B" is the same as "A is coinciding with some B," or A = BY.
*10

(17) Hence these coincides: "A is B," and "Some B coincides with A," or BY = A.

(18) A and AA and AAA, *etc.*, coincide from the nature of this *characteristica*, or "man" and "man man" and "man man man." Thus if someone be said to be man and animal alike, by "man" being analyzed into "rational animal" he is called in a similar manner "rational animal and animal," that is, "rational animal."

---

*10It is noteworthy that in place of A = BY one can also say A = AB, and thus there is no need to assume a new letter. Furthermore, this notation presupposes that AA is the same as A, for it is treated as a redundancy.

*11

(19) If A be B, B can be put in place of A in so far as being contained is concerned. For example, if A be B and B be C, A will be C. This is demonstrated from the nature of coincidence, for by coincidence they can be substituted for one another (unless in propositions which one could call "formal propositions," where one of the coincidents is assumed formally so that it is distinguished from the others; these propositions are in fact reflexive; and they are asserted not so much about a thing as about our manner of conceiving, where undoubtedly there is a distinction). Thus when (by 16) A = BY and B = CZ, therefore A =CYZ, or A contains C.

*12

(20) It should be noted that in this calculus it was to be assumed that in place of any number of letters whatsoever one letter can be put just as well, for example, YZ = X. But we have not yet used this in this calculus of reason lest confusion arise.

(21) Hereafter, I shall signify the definite by the first letters of the alphabet, the indefinite by the last, unless I indicate something different.

(22) One definite letter can be substituted for any number of definite letters; those things for which it has been substituted are the value or definition of it.

(23) An indefinite letter not yet used can be substituted for any definite letter. And so also for any number of definite letters, and for definite and indefinite letters, or A = Y can be put.

(24) A new indefinite letter can be joined to any letters whatever. For example, AY can be put in place of A. A = AA (by 18), and A is Y (or Y can be put in place of A, by 23); therefore A = AY.

---

*11Hence it is also evident that from AC = ABD it is not permissible to infer C = BD. It is evident also in A = AB that A cannot be omitted from both sides. If because AC = ABD it were possible to infer C = BD, it would be presupposed that nothing which is contained in A is contained also in C without being contained also in BD, and conversely.

*12It will be permissible also to have a certain general indefinite, such as "some being" or "something" (as we say in ordinary speech); then no coincidence results.

(25) That A is B (that A contains B) im-   [23 recto]
plies (contains) that some B is (contains) A.

$\overline{\text{A is B}} = \overline{\text{BY} = \text{A}}$ (by 17) $= \overline{\text{BY} = \text{AY}}$ (by 24) $=$ "Some B is A" (by 17).

(26) We must still call attention to certain things concerning this calculus which we should have said in advance; namely, that what is generally asserted or concluded, and not put forth just as an hypothesis regarding unspecified letters is to be understood with regard to any other letters as well. Thus if A = AA, it will also be possible to say B =BB.

(27) Some B = YB. And similarly A =ZA. Of course, one may say this in imitation of the former (by 26), but it is a new indefinite letter which must be assumed for the latter equation, namely, Z, just as a bit earlier it was Y.

(28) A term set forth by itself I customarily use for a universal, for example, "A is B," *i.e.*, "All A is B," for the concept B is contained in the concept A.

(29) "A is B"; therefore "Some A is B" (or *that A contains B* implies or contains that some A contains B). "A is B" = "AY is B" (by 24).

(30) That A is B and that B is A is the same as that A and B coincide, or that A coincides with B which coincides with A, for A = BY and B = AZ. Therefore, (by 31) A = AYZ. Therefore, the Y and Z are superflous, or Z is contained in A. Therefore, in place of B = AZ, one can say B = A.

(31) Of course, this too should be noted: if A = AY, then either Y is superfluous or is more general like "being," and can be safely omitted, like unity in multiplication according to the opinions of the arithmeticians; or Y is in A. Of course, Y always is in A, if one can say A = YA.

(32) *Negative proposition*: A does not contain B, or it is false that A is (contains) B.
*13
*14

---

*13*N. B.* If B is a proposition, "non-B" is the same as "B is false" or that "B" is false. Non-B, when B is understood to concern a proposition materially necessary, is either necessary or impossible. But this is not so in incomplexes.
*14I take "concept" then for incomplexes as well as for complexes; "term," for categorematic incomplexes.

(32a) B-non-B is impossible, or if B-non-B = C, C will be impossible.   *15

(33) Hence if A = non-B, AB will be impossible.

(34) What contains B-non-B is the same as the *impossible;* or EB-non-B is the same as the impossible.

(35) A *false proposition* is one which contains that AB contains non-B (B and A having been posited as possible). Moreover I understand B and Y with relation to terms as well as with relation to propositions.
*16

(36) A = B, therefore "A is B"; or "A = B" contains that A is B; for if Y be superfluous, it would become A = BY, *i.e.,* A = B. The same thing is shown in another way: A = B is the same as "A = BY and B = AY." Therefore A = B contains A = BY. Likewise, A = B, therefore AA = BA. Therefore, A is B.

(37) B is B. Now B = B (by 10); therefore, B is B (by 36).

(38) AB is B. This is indemonstrable and it is either an identity or a definition, either of the "is," or of "containing," or of a true proposition. It indicates that AB, or what contains B, is B or contains B.

(39) If B contains C, then AB contains C; for AB is B (by 38), B is C (by hypothesis); therefore (by 19), AB is C.

(40) A *true proposition* is either one which coincides with this: AB is B, or one which can be reduced to this fundamentally true proposition. (I think also that this can be applied to non-categorical propositions.)

(41) Therefore, since falsity is what is not true (by 3), it follows (from 40) that a false proposition is the same as a proposition which does not coincide with this: AB is B, or that a false proposition is the same as a proposition which cannot be proved.

Propositions of fact cannot always be proved by us, and therefore they are assumed like hypotheses.

(42) Of these propositions: "A contains   [23 verso]

---

*15"Impossible" in incomplexes is "non-being"; in complexes, it is "false."
*16That A contains B and that A contains C is the same as that A contains BC. Hence if A contains B, it also contains AB. Hence if AB contains non-B, AB also will contain AB-non-B.

B" and "A does not contain B," one is true, the other false; or they are *opposites*, for if one can be proved, the other can not be proved, provided the terms are possible. Therefore (by 41) they are not true or false at the same time.

(43) It is false that B contains non-B; or B does not contain non-B. In both instances this is evident from the preceding. For in whatever way you analyze them, this form always remains; "AB is B" never occurs. This is evident also from another proof: B contains B (by 37); therefore it does not contain non-B. Furthermore, this would be impossible (by 32).

(44) It is false that non-B contains B; this is evident in the same way.

(45) It is false that B and non-B coincide. This is evident from 43 and 44.

Furthermore, these presuppose that the term B is possible.

(46) It is false that AB contains non-B; or AB does not contain non-B. Furthermore, I suppose that AB is possible. This is shown like 43. AB contains B; therefore it does not contain non-B, because it is not impossible (by 32).
*17

(47) "A contains B" is a *universal affirmative proposition with regard to A* as the subject.

(48) "AY contains B" is a *particular affirmative proposition with regard to A.*

(49) If AB is C, it follows that AY is C, or it follows "Some A is C," for B = Y can be assumed by 23.

(50) "AY is not B" is a *universal negative proposition.*

(51) Hence it follows that a universal negative proposition and a particular affirmative proposition are opposites; or if one is true, the other is false (from 48 and 50).

(52) A particular affirmative proposition can be converted directly; or if some A is B, it follows that some B is A. I demonstrate this in this way: AY is B by hypothesis, i.e., (by 16) AY coincides with BY. Therefore (by 6) BY coincides with AY. Therefore (by 16) BY is A. *Q. E. D.*

---

*17Care should be taken lest we make use of syllogisms which we have not yet shown to be legitimate.

*18

(53) A universal negative proposition is converted directly; or if no A is B, it follows that no B is A. AY is not B (by hypothesis). Therefore AY does not coincide with BY (by 16). Therefore BY does not coincide with AY (by 6). Therefore (by 16) BY is not A. *Q. E. D.*

(54) A universal affirmative proposition is converted *per accidents;* or if all A is B, it follows that some B is A. A is B by hypothesis. Therefore some A is B (by 29). Therefore (by 52) some B is A. The same thing more briefly is: A coincides with BY (by 16). Therefore BY coincides with A (by 6). Therefore (by 36) BY is A. It will be worthwhile to compare these two demonstrations, so that it is clear whether they come to the same thing or actually reveal the truth of some proposition which up to this point has been assumed without a demonstration.

*19

*20

(55) If A contains B and A is true, B is true also. By a false letter I understand either a false term (either one which is impossible, or one which is non-being) or a false proposition. Also, similarly by true may be understood a possible term or a true proposition. Further, as I shall explain later, a whole syllogism is in my view also a proposition. The rest of what I am declaring here can also be expressed in this way: any part of the true is true, or what is contained in the true is true.

This can be demonstrated from the following:

(56) *True* in general I define in this say: A is *true*, if we put A's value in place of A, and again treat anything whatever which enters into the value of A just as A has been treated, and if, when this can be done, B and non-B, or a contradic-

---

18"Fundamental or undemonstrated propositions may be designated by capital letters, for example, LI (or at the same time by ordinary and diverse numbers).

*19"Something needs to be said about the comparison of these: "No A is B" and "All A is non-B."

*20"Thus concerning conversion through contraposition of the universal affirmative proposition, instead of "No A is B" may we not say "All A is not B"?

tion, never occurs. From this it follows that in order for us to be certain of the truth either the analysis must be continued all the way to the fundamentally true (at least either to a truth dealt with by such a process, or to a truth which is established as true)—or it must be demonstrated either from the progression of the analysis itself or from a certain general relation among the analyses preceding and the one following that such a contradiction will never occur no matter how far the analysis is carried. This is extremely noteworthy, for in this way we can often eliminate a long continuation. It can also be the case that the very analysis of the letters entails something about the analyses of what follows, for example here, the analysis of truth. Also it is problematical whether each analysis must necessarily end in fundamental truths or in unanalyzables, especially in the case of contingent propositions, since one cannot reduce them to identities.

(57) *False in general* I define as what is not   [24 recto] true [or what contains terms in which B and non-B occur]. In order to establish that something is false, it is necessary to show either that it is the opposite of true, or that it contains the opposite of true, or that it contains a contradiction, or B and non-B; or, if it be demonstrated that it cannot in any way be shown by a continued analysis that it is true, then it is false.

(58) Thus what contains the false is false.

(59) It can however contain something true, and nevertheless be false, namely, if (by 58) it contains something false as well.

NECESSARY AND CONTINGENT TRUTHS (24 recto, sec. 60-25 recto, sec. 70)

(60) Hence we also seem able to discern a distinction between necessary truths and others; for example, necessary truths are those which can be reduced to identities, or the opposites of which may be reduced to contradictions. Impossibles are those which may be reduced to contradictions, or the opposites of which may be reduced to identities.

(61) Those truths are possible concerning which it can be shown that in their analysis a contradiction would never

arise. Contingent truths are those which although their analysis be continued into infinity lack resolution. Furthermore contingent falsehoods are those whose falsity can be shown in no other way than by our being unable to demonstrate that they are true. It seems to be uncertain whether it is sufficient for demonstrating truth that it be certain that no contradiction will occur by continuing the analysis. It follows from this that every possible is true. For my part I call an incomplex term which is possible "true," and one which is impossible I call "false." But there is some uncertainty with regard to a complex term such as "A contains B" or "A is B." Nevertheless I conceive of the analysis of a complex term as an analysis into other complex terms. Obviously when it is the case that $\overline{A \text{ is } B} = L$, $B = CD$, $\overline{A \text{ is } C} = M$, and $\overline{A \text{ is } D} = N$, it is certain that $L = MN$. Nevertheless, though a subject A be analyzed, a mere part of A's value cannot be substituted for A, but the whole value must be substituted; I give warning of this in passing. If $C = EG$ and $D = FG$, and $A = EFG$, M will be analyzable into these two: $\overline{A = EFG} = P$ and $\overline{EFG = EG} = Q$, or there will be $M = PQ$; and similarly N will be analyzable into these two: $\overline{A = EFG} = P$, and $EFG = FG = R$. Therefore $L = PQR$. These are fundamental, true propositions, for P is an hypothesis, namely, a definition or experiential proposition; R and Q are the first axioms. But yet if we would go on from this point the definition must be established as possible; or A must be shown to be possible, or EFG must be shown not to involve a contradiction, i.e., not to involve X-non-X. If it is established that A exists, or has existed, and to such a degree is possible (or at least that something similar to A has existed, although in fact perhaps this event cannot be obtained, for two complete things never are similar, and with regard to incomplete things it is sufficient that one of the two similars exist so that what is incomplete, i.e, the common denominator, be called "possible" (Nevertheless this seems to be useful, or if one sphere has existed, it will be possible to say immediately that any sphere is possible.)), this cannot be known except by experience.*21 From this it is evident

---

*21That of which the similar is possible, is itself also possible.

that this matter progresses in the same way in complex terms and in incomplex ones. To prove that a complex term is true is to reduce it to other true complex terms, and these in turn to complex terms which are fundamental, true terms, *i.e.*, to axioms (or propositions known *per se*), definitions of incomplex terms which have been proved to be true, and experiential propositions. In the same way incomplex terms are proved true by reducing them to other true incomplex terms, and these in turn to other incomplex terms which are fundamental, true terms, *i.e.*, to terms conceived *per se*, or to terms which we have proved (or to terms which are similar to terms which we have proved. However this need not be added, for it can be demonstrated by one of the similars having possible existence that the others also are possible.) Thus the result is that every analysis of complex terms as well as of incomplex terms ends in axioms, terms conceived *per se*, and experiential propositions. Moreover, this analysis is made by substituting its value in place of anything whatever. Also, when the contained is substituted for the containing, an indefinite value is substituted, for example, as we have shown above in number 16.

(62) Moreover, every true proposition can be proved. Since experiential propositions are also true propositions, then if no other means is given for proving them than the one described just previously, it follows that experiential propositions are analyzable also into axioms, terms conceived *per se*, and experiential propositions; however, no primitive experiential propositions can be given, unless they are themselves known *per se*, or axioms. [24 verso]

(63) We are inquiring whether experiential propositions are analyzable into other experiential propositions without limit, and—leaving experiential propositions out of discussion —whether it be possible that a certain proof be such that the proof of a proposition is always ascertained to presuppose the proof of another proposition which is neither an axiom nor a definition, and to the same extent in turn itself requires proof. Thus certain incomplex terms must also be analyzable continuously in this way so that one never arrives at *per se* concepts. In general, it will be clear from an absolute analysis

whether a virtual coincidence becomes formal or explicit, or whether the matter reduces to an identity.

(64) Thus we are inquiring whether it is possible for the analysis of incomplex terms ever to be continued without limit so that one never arrives at *per se* concepts. To be sure, if no concepts conceived *per se* which can be conceived clearly are given us, or only one (for example, the concept of being), it follows that no proposition can be demonstrated perfectly by reason; for although from the posited definitions and axioms it is completely demonstrable without experiential propositions, nevertheless the definitions presuppose the possibility of the terms and to that degree an analysis either into concepts *per se* or into those disclosed wholly in experience. Therefore one comes back to experiential propositions or to other propositions.

(65) But if we say that a continuation of the analysis without limit is possible, then it can at least be seen whether the progression in analyzing it is reducible to some rule. Also, in a proof of complex terms in which incomplex terms analyzable without limit are constituents, the rule of such a progression will appear along with the proof.

(66) And, moreover, if by the continued analysis of the predicate and the continued analysis of the subject, it is never possible to demonstrate a coincidence; but, on the other hand, from the continued analysis and the progression thereby generated and the rule of the progression, it at least never appears that a contradiction must arise, the proposition is possible. And if it appears from the rule of the progression in analyzing it to that extent that the matter is brought to the point that the difference between those things which ought to coincide is less than any given difference, the proposition will have been shown to be true; but if on the contrary there appears from the progression some such thing as ought never to arise, the proposition is shown to be false—in the case of necessary propositions.
*22

---

*22It is not clear whether everything is true which cannot be proved false, or everything false which cannot be proved true. Well then, what about those things concerning which neither is the case? It should be said that both truth and falsity can always be proved, at least by an endless

(67) Moreover a proposition whose opposite is not possible, or whose opposite when it is assumed leads by means of an analysis to a contradiction, is necessary. Thus, a necessary proposition is one which is demonstrable by means of identities and definitions without any additional application of experiential propositions other than that needed to establish that a term is possible.

(68) But in addition we must examine that source from which I know that I am proceeding correctly in giving a definition; for if I say A = EFG, I ought to know not only that E, F, G, as singulars are possible, but also that they are compatible with one another. However, it is evident that this knowledge cannot be gained except by experience either of the thing in question or of another thing which is similar to the thing in question in at least that respect with which we are concerned. But if someone says that I can know this at least from the ideas comprehended in my mind while I am aware that I am conceiving of EFG—which I call A—I reply that I can, when I say that I am conceiving   [25 recto] of E, either conceive of something which I experience to involve nothing else, or conceive of something composite which I apprehend confusedly. If I experience E to involve nothing else or to be conceived *per se*, then one can admit that it itself is possible. But concerning such matters absolutely no propositions are possible except identities; otherwise I have said falsely that I have experienced what involves nothing else. If I experience E to involve additional things, they must be extracted similarly in turn; as many times as I connect together the additional things which are not conceived *per se* I need an experience, not only because I conceive them simultaneously

---

analysis. But then it is contingent, or it is possible that it be true or that it be false; and it is the same with regard to concepts, so that in an endless analysis they appear true or false; *i.e.*, they must be admitted to the realm of existence or they must not. *N. B.* whether by this method a true concept will be one which exists; a false one, one which does not exist. Every impossible concept is false, but not every possible one is true; and so the false will be what neither is nor will be, for example: A proposition of a certain kind is false; *etc.* This will be the case unless perhaps we prefer to have no principle of existence in them; a true concept here will be the same as a possible one; a false concept the same as an impossible one, unless when we say, for example, "*Pegasus existing.*"

in the same subject—for such a concept is confused—but also because in fact they will have existed in the same subject.

(69) Thus, it is among the first principles that terms which we understand to exist in the same subject do not involve a contradiction; or if A is B, and A is C, undoubtedly BC is possible or does not involve a contradiction.

(70) God, out of the experiences of his own understanding alone, without any perception of others, judges concerning the possibility of things.

THE DEFINITION OF "EXISTING"; THE COMPLETE CONCEPT
(25 recto, sec. 71-25 verso, sec. 74)

(71) Something must be said concerning the propositions "A is existing" or "A has existed." For example, if I say concerning an existing thing "A is B," this is the same as if I say "AB existing"; for instance, "Peter is denying," *i.e.*, "Peter the denying is existing." Here we seek to learn how we should proceed in this analyzing, or whether the term "Peter the denying" involves existence; whether "Peter existing" involves denial; whether "Peter" involves both existence and denial, as if you were to say "Peter is denying in actuality," or "denying as existing"—which is certainly true. In general, it should be said that this distinction is between the individual or complete term, and another; for if I say "Some man is denying," "man" does not contain "denial," for it is an incomplete term, and "man" does not contain all the things which can be said about him as an individual man.

(72) If there be BY, and the indefinite term Y be superfluous, or, for instance, "some Alexander the Great" and "Alexander the Great" be the same, then B is an *individual*.*23

(73) But we are trying to find out what the word "existing" signifies, for at the least "existing" is being or the possible, plus something else. Further, all things considered, I do not see that anything else is conceived in "existing" than some degree of being, since it can be applied to various beings. However, I am unwilling to say that that something exists

---

*23If there be the term BA, and B be an individual, A will be superfluous, or if BA = C, there will be B = C.

is possible or that existence is possible, for this is nothing
other than its very essence; further, we understand existence
as actual or something added over and above the possibility
or essence, so that in this sense "possible existence" would be
the same as cutting off actuality from actuality, which is
absurd. Therefore I maintain that "existence" is being which
is compatible with the most other things. Or it is being in
the highest degree possible, and so all co-existents are equally
possible. Or, what amounts to the same thing, existence is
what is acceptable to a perceptive and pro- [25 verso]
ficient one; but he himself is thus presupposed to exist. It
will be definable minimally as: that exists which is acceptable
to the mind of another, and is not displeasing to another
more powerful mind, if any minds are supposed to exist.
And so therefore the matter amounts to saying that what is
not displeasing to the most powerful mind, if a most powerful mind be assumed to exist, exists. But so that this definition
can be applied to experiences, it must rather be defined in
this way: that exists which pleases another (existing) mind
("existing" ought not to be appended, if we are looking for
a definition, not a simple proposition), and is (absolutely)
not displeasing to the most powerful mind. However, it is
more pleasing to a mind that that happen which has a reason
than that which does not have a reason. Thus, if the many
are A, B, C, D and one of these is to be chosen, and B, C, D
are similar throughout, but A alone is distinguished from the
others in some aspect, then A will be pleasing to any mind
which discerns this. It is the same even if there is no distinction
among B, C, and D, but the distinction is between A and the
others; and though the mind have decreased alternatives of
choice, it will choose A. Nevertheless it chooses freely, because it can inquire whether or not there be a distinction
among B, C, D.

(74) All existential propositions are certainly true, but
they are not necessary, for they cannot be proved except by
using infinities or by a continuous analysis involving an infinite number of facts, namely, only from a complete notion
of an individual, which involves infinite existence. Thus if I
say "Peter denies," with this understood in relation to a certain time, the nature of that time is presupposed too, which

also involves every existent at that time, If I say "Peter denies" in an unrestricted way by abstracting it from time so that it is true whether he has denied or will deny, then the matter must be nonetheless demonstrated from the concept of Peter. But the concept of Peter is complete, and what is more it involves infinity; therefore we can never arrive at a perfect proof. However, we always more and more nearly approximate it so that the difference is less than any given.

THE STATEMENT OF PROPOSITIONS IN THE FORM OF TERMS, AND OF HYPOTHETICAL PROPOSITIONS IN THE FORM OF CATEGORICAL PROPOSITIONS (25 verso, sec. 75)

(75) If, as I hope, I am able to conceive all propositions in the form of terms, and hypothetical propositions in the form of categorical propositions, and to treat them all without exception, this state of affairs assures an extraordinary facility in my *characteristica* and analysis of concepts, and it will be an invention of great moment. Generally I call a term false which in incomplexes is an impossible term, or at least meaningless, and which in complexes is an impossible proposition, or at least a proposition which cannot be proved. Thus the analogy remains. By A I understand either an incomplex term, or a proposition, or a grouping, or a grouping of groupings, *etc.*, so that generally a term is true which can be understood perfectly.

THE DEFINITION OF "WHOLE," "PART," "CONTINUUM," AND "NUMBER" (25 verso, sec. 76-*[25]*)

(76) Besides the term "being" we shall also employ "beings," from which a whole and its parts are produced, and, generally, if A is not B and B is not A, and the primitive is this: "A is L" and "B is L" is the same as "C is L," then C is said to be a whole; A (or B), a part. It is possible to be in doubt whether and to what extent C is one real being; whether or not one being always results from many, even when they have been dispersed; and indeed when it does or does not result.

*24
*25

THE USE OF "*Non*" (26 recto, sec. 76a-27 recto, sec. 106)

(76a) Non-A is non-$\overline{AB}$, or non-A $=$ ___ [26 recto]
Y-non-AB. "Every non-man is a non-rational-man." This
follows from 77.

(77) Generally "A is B" is the same as "Non-B is non-A."
The preceding demonstration is from this, for AB is A. Therefore, non-A is non-AB. We need to see whether this can be
demonstrated. It is to be demonstrated under 95 and 99.

(78) "A $=$ B" and "non-A $=$ non-B" coincide.

(79) But if A be B, it does not follow that non-A is
non-B; or if man be an animal, it does not follow that non-
man is non-animal. Although B can be substituted for A, still
it is not for that reason permissible to substitute non-B for
non-A, unless A in turn can be substituted for B.

(80) We ought to see whether we can do without infinities. It seems reasonable that non-A is the same as that which is
not A, or the subject of a negative proposition whose predicate is A, or all which is not A. Thus, if $\overline{Y}$ is not A, there
will be $\overline{Y} =$ non-A, or "$\overline{Y} \neq AX$" is the same as "$\overline{Y} =$
non-A."

(81) $\overline{Y}$ or the indefinite Y with a little line I take as
signifying "any one without distinction"; Y is an indeterminate
one, $\overline{Y}$ is any one without distinction.

(82) Also one will be able to say: "B is not A" is the
same as "B is non-A." From this, "B $\neq AY$" is the same as
"B $=$ Y-non-A."

(83) Generally "A is B" is the same as "A $=$ AB," for it
has been shown that B is contained in A; and man and man-
animal are the same. I have already noted this above in the
margin of section 16, and though "Man is a rational animal
animal" seems to follow from that, still "animal animal" is
the same as "animal," as I have noted above at section 18.

(84) Hence if the proposition "A is B" is said to be false

---

*24Continuum: when parts are indefinite.
*25Number arises if we consider only that beings are many, but not
of what kind they are.

or is denied, then that is to say "A ≠ AB," *i.e.*, "Some A is not B."

(85) That A is non-B is the same as to say "A = A-non-B." This is evident from 83. If you say "A = A-non-B" is false or "A ≠ A-non-B," it signifies "Some A is B."

(86) Further, non-B is the same as that which is not B, or a genus whose species are A, C, D, *etc.*, with A posited not to be B, C not to be B, D not to be B.

(87) Thus that no A is B is the same as that A is non-B, or that any A is one of those which are not B; or "AY ≠ ABY" is the same as "A = A-non-B." Therefore we have a link between affirmative and negative infinities.

(88) As I say elsewhere, generally that A is AB is the same as that A coincides with AB (or if the proposition "A is AB" be true, it will be reciprocal). I demonstrate this in the following way: A is AB by hypothesis, *i.e.*, (by 83) A = AAB, *i.e.*, (by 18) A = AB. Likewise, A is AB (by hypothesis), and AB is A (by 38). Therefore (by 30) A = AB. These two demonstrations may be compared with one another, for either they will end in the same place, or they will give a demonstration of some proposition which has been assumed without proof.

(89) Let us consider a particular affirmative proposition: "Some animal is a man." BY = AZ. That also can be changed into this: BY = ABY, or one can say that "some animal is a man" is the same as "some animal is a man-animal." This is evident from 83. It is of no importance that Y is uncertain, for—whatever that may be—it is conceived to be known, and to be present; then reasoning has a place.

(90) But although an indefinite Y can al-   [26 verso] ways be avoided in the predicate in this way, it is still not avoidable in the subject, and it is better for it to remain in the predicate, because of the clearer inversion. In general, be cause the indefinites cannot be absolutely eliminated, it is better to leave them.
    *26

(91) A is B, then A is not non-B. Let it be true that A is non-B—if in fact it is possible. Moreover, A is B by

---

*26On the contrary, I think that they can be eliminated.

hypothesis. Therefore A is B-non-B, which is absurd. Add under 100.

*27

(92) This consequence is not valid: If A is not non-B, then A is B; or, it is false that every animal is non-man, but nevertheless it does not follow that every animal is a man.

(93) If A is B, non-B is non-A. Let it be false—if possible —that non-B is non-A, or that non-B is not A; then it will be true that non-B is A. Therefore some A is non-B. Therefore it is false that all A is B, contrary to the hypothesis.

(94) If non-B is non-A, A is B. Let it be false, if possible, that A is B. Therefore A will be non-B. Therefore some non-B will be A (by conversion). Therefore, it is false that some non-B is non-A (by 91). Therefore it is all the more false that all non-B is non-A, contrary to the hypothesis.

(95) That A is B is the same as that non-B is non-A; this is evident from 93 and 94 in conjunction with 30. We ought to see whether or not proposition 95 can be demonstrated *per se*, without 93 and 94; this is evident in section 99.

(96) Non-non-A = A.

(97) "No A is B" is the same as "A is non-B" (by 87).

*28

(99) "A is B" is the same as "A is non-non-B" (by 96), and this is the same (by 87) as "No A is non-B" (87), *i.e.*, "No non-B is A" (by conversion of a universal negative), *i.e.*, (by 87) "All non-B is non-A" = "A is B." Q. E. D.

(100) If A is B, it follows that A is not non-B, or it is false that all A is non-B. For if A is B, then no A is non-B, or it is false that some A is non-B (by 87). Therefore (by 101) it is all the more false that all A is non-B. Add 91.

(101) If it is false that some A is B, "All A is B" is false, or—what is the same—some A is not B. Therefore all A is not B. It is posited—if possible—that all A is B. Therefore some A is B (by 29). But this is contrary to the hypothesis,

---

*27This way of reasoning or reducing to the absurd has already been established in the preceding.

*28(98) "All A is B" is the same as "No A is non-B," or that some A is not non-B. This is evident from 97 or 87 by merely putting non-B for B and by putting non-non-B or B for non-B.

and to that degree false; therefore the previous proposition also is false.

(102) If A is B and A is C, it is the same   [27 recto] as A is BC.

(103) If A is non-B, and A is non-C, it is the same as A is non-B-non-C.

(104) Non-B is non-$\overline{BC}$. This has been demonstrated in 76a. But non-$\overline{BC}$ is not always non-B. One might wish that a standard of a formal, or general, proposition had been devised, as if I were to say: It is false that every composite negative is a simple negative, or non-$\overline{YX}$ ≠ non-$\overline{Y}$, on condition that $\overline{Y}$ and $\overline{X}$ signify any things standing in a similar relation to each other.

(105) If A is non-$\overline{BC}$ it does not on that account follow either that A is non-B, or that A is non-C, for it is possible that B is = LM and C = NP, and that A is non-LN, in which case A will be non-$\overline{LMNP}$ or non-$\overline{BC}$. However, from this it follows that it is false that at the same time A is B and A is C, or that A is BC. This is evident from 91 or 100.

(106) From this it is evident that "*non*" ought to be separated as little as possible from its letter or the formula in which it is set forth in the calculus.

A SCHEMATIC REPRESENTATION OF PROPOSITIONS AND TERMS
(27 recto, sec. 107-27 verso, sec. 111)

(107) All multiplication of propositions can thus be represented generally as $\overline{ABCD}$ *etc.* We can say that $\overline{AB}$ = L, $\overline{LC}$ = M, $\overline{MD}$ = N by positing that some of them can be analyzed in a similar manner, for example, L or M or N; and those into which they themselves are analyzed can in turn perhaps be analyzed in this way as occasion arises. However, a line drawn above, for example, $\overline{AB}$, can signify affirmation or negation, or rather coincidence or non-coincidence, and the little line can have a signification in the middle as well as in the extremes; in the middle to signify the mode of the proposition, whether affirmative or negative, *etc.*; in the extreme at which B is under consideration a little line will designate the same for B. And thus if there be:

4	5	6
1	2	3
A	B	C

locus 1 will designate the quantity or the quality, *etc.*, in accordance with which the term A is employed here or the manner of employment of the term A; locus 2, the nature of the proposition AB; locus 3, the mode of term B; locus 4, the mode of employing the whole $\overline{AB}$ or L; locus 5, the nature of the proposition $\overline{ABC}$ or $\overline{LC}$; locus 6, the mode of term C. It should be possible to observe a sort of order in the numbers so that one always begins at the most subdivided or at the lowest level of the subdivided or at the terms nearer to the incomplex, for example, if there were:

13			14			15	⊙
10		11		12			
	7		8		9		
		1	2	3	4	5	6
A	B	C		D	E		F

From this it is understandable that the relations and denominations of terms can be altered in extraordinary ways as much by the order, if you regard only the arrangement of numbers, as by the value of each number, if the locus be treated in terms of quantity or quality alone.

(108) Every term, even an incomplex term, can be understood as a proposition, as if to it had been added the phrase "this being," just as "man" can be understood as if one were to say "Man is the same as this being," namely, it itself is what is, or, more generally, just as if there had been added the word "truth," *e.g.*, "Man is the truth," "Man is an animal, is this truth." The "this truth" has served a function here which unity serves in arithmetic, *i.e.*, to supply loci or dimensions. If it be assumed that whatever is connected with another thing is subdivided in as many ways as it is connected with that thing, and if a term is not assumed to be joined except to an equally incomplex or complex one, then truth or unity is written "V." From ⊙ ☽

29 would be made where the loci have been supplied, for it can be said that A is the same as this truth is the same as "this truth is this truth"; but it should be noted that the V itself anywhere that it is supplied ought to be changed: A = "A is true" or A = truth.

(109) Furthermore, just as any term can be   [27 verso] conceived in the form of a proposition, as we have explained, so also any proposition can be conceived in the form of a term, like: that man is an animal is true, is a proposition, is some such a thing, is a cause, is a reason, *etc.* These represent the most universal propositions which have been discovered concerning these multiplications.

(110) Furthermore new reflexive terms can be made which can be dealt with in a manner similar to direct ones; for example, the subject of such a proposition, "such a . . .," can be called by some name. We ought to see how in turn we can explain these and the denominations among one another by letters. For example, if the subject of a universal affirmative proposition be the predicate of another affirmative proposition whose subject is the predicate of the first, the subject is said to be the same as the predicate of the same proposition. If, however, anyone be willing to express the matter rigorously according to the common practice of logic or even of men as they ordinarily speak in propositions he meets with considerable difficulty; for example, if he wants to say "the subject of a universal affirmative proposition, whose predicate is the subject of a universal affirmative proposition, in which the subject is the predicate of the preceding proposition, is the same as the predicate of the proposition mentioned of which its predicate is the subject." Thus the relative "mentioned" or "preceding" cannot be avoided. If A is B and B is A, how much more satisfactorily, briefly, and clearly we say "A is the same as B." Furthermore, its proof can easily be given in the same way as we gave it above, *i.e.*, by the

*29

43				⟩ 44					45
37		38		39	40		41		42
25	26	27 28	29	30	31	32	33 34	35	36
1 2 3 4	5 6 7	8	9 10 11 12		13 14 15	16 17	18 19 20	21 22	23 24
A V V	V B	V C	D		E V V	V F	V V	V

use of letters. But in the case of words there would no doubt be enough perplexity, and it would be necessary to use special care in placing them directly. If they are put together properly, I believe that they will be clear, although I do not know whether the consequences also are easily drawn as clearly in like manner from the letters; for example, it is evident here that just as we have said that A is the same as A, so also B can be said to be the same as B. This does not seem to be made manifest as easily by the use of words.

(111) We ought to note that even in the case of the whole series of an analysis certain generalities can be discovered about its process, even if the analysis be continued endlessly; and with regard to these things suitable reflexive words can be devised also—even certain general letters, for example, $\overline{Y}$. But it will appear more clearly in progress which of them is preferable.

THE NEGATION OF PROPOSITIONS (28 recto, sec. 112-*[30])

(112) We ought to see whether or not Y   [28 recto] is taken in a somewhat different sense when one says "AY is B," i.e., "Some A is B," than when it is denied that any A is B, with the result that it is not only denied that some A is B or that this indeterminate A is B, but also that any A whatever from among the indeterminate ones is B, so that when it is said that no A is B, the sense is that it is denied that $A\overline{Y}$ is B. Of course, $\overline{Y}$ is Y, or "any Y whatever" will contain "this Y." Thus when I say "Some A is B," I am saying "This particular A is B." If I deny that some A is B, or that this particular A is B, to such a degree I seem to be asserting a particular negative. But when I deny that any A whatever is B, or that not only this A, but also this A and this A is B, then I deny that $\overline{Y}A$ is B. Also, when one speaks, to deny that some A is B, or to say that some A is not B, does not seem to mean that no A is B; similarly, to say "All A is not B" does not seem to mean the negation of the statement that all A is B, but it does seem to mean that it

---

*[30]Universal affirmative proposition: A is equal to B with something added. Universal negative proposition: it is denied.

is being said concerning any A which is not B. More basic than these is the fact that the negation of a universal affirmative proposition is a particular negative proposition. Thus, the negation of a particular affirmative proposition cannot also be a particular negative proposition (for the negation of a particular affirmation proposition and the negation of a universal affirmative proposition cannot be the same). Therefore, there is left only the possibility that it is a universal negative proposition; and it cannot be anything else.

A LINEAR REPRESENTATION OF A, E, I, AND O PROPOSITIONS
(28 recto, sec. 113-sec. 123)

(113) The matter will be easily shown by figures. "A is B" or "A coincides with a certain B".

A |———————————| or A coincides
B |━━━━━━- - - - - - -| with AB
*31

*32

(114) "Some A is B," or "Some A coincides with some B":

A - - - - - - ——————— ━━━━━━━ — - - - -
B - - - - - - - - - ━━━━━ ———————— - - -

(115) Hence A = A. No doubt generally we ought to arrange these as if the lines parallel to the horizontal, of which one has been drawn below the other in order to distinguish them, were drawn one super-imposed upon the other.

(116) AB = BY, where I understand by Y whatever is in the whole line B which falls under A.

---

*31 A small perpendicular line signifies the limits beyond which the terms cannot, and within which they can, be extended in a sound proposition or arrangement.

*32 Just as a small perpendicular line signifies the maximum, so a two-fold horizontal line signifies the minimum or what cannot be taken away in a sound arrangement. A two-fold line does not seem necessary in the subject but only in the predicate; for I select the subject arbitrarily. In place of a two-fold line I prefer a heavier one. For example, when ——————————— a line is drawn very near under a line this is understood to compose one term, although —————————— one term can also always be understood in the case of lines drawn standing further apart.

(117) A = BY is the same as A = BA.

(118) A = BY, therefore BY = AY.

(119) A = BY and B = AY, is the same as A = B.

AB in general
A____
B ____
All this is evident from an inspection of the figure.

(120) The negation of this: Some A is B; or when it is denied that some A coincides with some B, it is expressed in this way:

A _ _ _ _ ____
B ____ _ _ _ _

(121) But the negation of this: "All A is B" is expressed in this way:

A _ _ _ _ _ ____
B _ _ _ _ _ _ _ ____ _ _ _

(122) We can introduce also the other consideration: that we not hold the genus to be a part of the species, as we did above on the ground that the concept of genus is part of (or at least included in) the concept of species; but that, on the contrary, the species is a part of the genus, since the individuals of the species are a part of (or at least included in) the individuals of a genus.

(123) Thus "All A is B" will be represented in this way:

A |==== _ _ _ _ ‑|⎫
                     ⎬ All A is B
B |_____ ⎭

This representation is the inverse of the earlier one. In the same way the representation of a particular negative proposition is the inverse of the earlier one. But a particular affirmative proposition and a universal negative proposition are represented in the same manner as before because it is of no importance whether one places the lines before or after. Thus generally it can be said that the earlier representation differs from the latter in this respect at least: the lines in the figure are transposed.

A Numerical (Algebraic) Representation of Propositions
(28 verso, sec. 124-*38)

(124) There is also another way of representing propositions: by means of numbers. By putting num-

[28 verso]

bers for terms, the universal affirmative proposition "A is B" signifies: A (or at least the square of A or the cube) is divisible by B. A and AB are here understood to be the same.

(125) The particular affirmative proposition "Some A is B" signifies that A multiplied by B or AB can be divided by B. It is understood, of course, that AB is always divisible by A, unless in AB A is destroyed; if, for example, A were to signify $\frac{C}{B}$ and C could not be divided by B.

(126) The particular negative proposition is that it is false that A is divisible by B, although perhaps AB can be divided by B.

(127) The universal negative proposition is that it is false that AB is divisible by B. The cause of this is nothing else than the fact that A contains $\frac{1}{B}$

Thus strictly speaking it is a universal negative proposition if A contains non-B; consequently there is agreement that the universal negative proposition is the opposite of the particular affirmative proposition. Of course, if A is divided by B, A cannot be multiplied by B.
*33

(128) Therefore, we have these expressions: A = AB is a universal affirmative proposition. AB = AB is a particular affirmative proposition; if the particular affirmative proposition be false, the former also is false, since in that case AB is an impossible term because A contains non-B. A = A-non-B is a universal negative proposition. From this it follows that the particular affirmative proposition is false, or AB is an impossible term—or rather false (for if this cannot be demonstrated perfectly by analyzing it into infinity, it is false, not impossible). Then the particular negative proposition is A-non-B = A-non-B. And this I know from considering numbers. Thus finally we have plainly eliminated the indefinite Y. And this we know from numbers.

(129) All things can be demonstrated by numbers, if this one thing is observed: that AA and A are equivalent, and that $\frac{A}{A}$ is not admitted, because multiplication here represents a complexity of concepts. If, however, some concept be joined directly to its own self, for example, "man man," nothing is formed but "man." Division however repre-

---

*33All things can be demonstrated by numbers, if only this be observed.

sents the negation of one with regard to the other, when it does not come out exactly. Thus when A is divisible exactly by B, or when A contains B, then there is represented the universal affirmative proposition "A is B." When A is divisible exactly by non-B or $\frac{1}{B}$ or when A contains the fraction $\frac{1}{B}$ (which represents non-B), a universal negative proposition is represented. But when A is not divided exactly by B a particular negative proposition arises, and when A is not divided exactly by $\frac{1}{B}$ a particular affirmative proposition arises. Thus I have uncovered that secret upon which I had brooded in vain several years before.

*34

*35

*36

*37

*38

---

*34Negation must be distinguished from division. Division is the omission of some term, but it is not therefore negation, except indeed in the case of infinites, because it denies what is not contained in the term. Thus in the case of a formula division or taking away will be distinguished from negation; but from the point of view of reality it is not to be distinguished.

"A = A" is true	"A = A:A" is false
A = A	A ≠ A:A
A = AB Universal affirmative	Either A:B ≠ A:B or A:B is false
A = A:B Universal negative	Either AB ≠ AB or AB is false
AB = AB Particular affirmative	Or A ≠ A:B
A:B = A:B Particular negative	Or A ≠ AB

*35Here I understand that a certain man is learned if only this be possible, for here we are considering abstract concepts, not experiences. If A = BY be possible, that BY is some B which is A. Thus if the particular affirmative proposition is false, it is impossible that such a concept be given.

*36It seems best that we define particulars as we did previously; namely, AB is a true concept or AB = AB is a particular affirmative proposition.

*37Also, A:B is a true concept or A:B = A:B is a particular negative proposition.

*38When we say that AB is a false concept, or we deny a particular affirmative proposition, it becomes a universal negative proposition. When we say A:B is a false concept, or "A:B ≠ A:B," it becomes a universal affirmative proposition. Hence the conversion of a universal negative proposition and a particular affirmative proposition is directly evident at once. But from this we must presently show that A = AB follows if A:B ≠ A:B, and that A = A:B follows if AB ≠ AB.

TRUE AND FALSE CONCEPTS: TRUE AND FALSE, POSSIBLE AND IMPOSSIBLE, NECESSARY AND CONTINGENT PROPOSITIONS (28 verso, sec. 130-29 recto, sec. 136)

(130) Further, a true proposition is one which can be proven. A false proposition is one which is not true. An impossible proposition is one in which a contradictory term is an ingredient. A possible proposition is one which is not impossible. Is therefore each universal negative proposition impossible? This seems to be the case because it is understood with regard to concepts, not with regard to existing things. For example, if I say that no man is an animal, I do not understand this with regard to existing men only, but it follows from this also that what is denied regarding some singular such as Peter is denied of him necessarily. Therefore it must be denied that every universal negative proposition is impossible, and to an objection we can reply: That A contains non-B is proved either by demonstration or by a perfect analysis, or only by an analysis continuable into infinity or always imperfect. Thus, it is certain, but not in fact necessary, because it can never be reduced to an identity or its opposite to a contradiction.

(130a) Therefore the true is that which   [29 recto] can be proved, or whose reason can be assigned by an analysis. The false is what is contrary. The necessary is what is reduced by an analysis to an identity. The impossible is what is reduced by an analysis to a contradiction. The false is a term or a proposition which contains things proved in any way whatever to be opposed. The impossible is what contains things proved opposed through a finite reduction. Thus, for example, $A = AB$, if the proof has been given through a finite analysis, ought to be distinguished from $A = AB$, if the proof has been given by an endless analysis. From this there arises already the consideration of necessary, possible, impossible, and contingent.

(131) The analysis is made on two bases, either that of concepts in the mind, without an experience (except reflection, because we conceive in this way), or that of perceptions or experientials. The former is not in need of proof; it does not presuppose a new proposition, and up to this point the

true is whatever I clearly and distinctly perceive is true; the latter presupposes the truth of an experience. In GOD, only the analysis of proper concepts is required, which becomes a whole at once in his presence. From this he knows the truths even of contingent propositions, whose demonstration transcends every finite intellect.

(132) Each true proposition can be proved, since the predicate is in the subject, as Aristotle says, or the concept of the predicate is involved in the concept of the subject completely understood; in any case the truth must be demonstrable by an analysis of the terms into their values or into those terms which they contain.

(133) A necessary true proposition can be proved by reduction to identities, or of its opposite to contradictories; whence the opposite is called impossible.

(134) A contingent true proposition cannot be reduced to identities; notwithstanding it is proved, by its being shown by a continued gradual analysis that it approaches identities continuously, but that it never reaches them. Whence it belongs to GOD alone, who embraces the whole infinite with his mind, to know the certainty of all contingent truths.

(135) For this reason, the discrimination of necessary truths from contingent ones is the same as that of intersecting and asymptotic lines, or commensurable and incommensurable numbers.

(136) But a difficulty stands in the way: we can demonstrate that one line perpetually approaches another, e. g., an asymptote, and that two quantities are equal to one another; furthermore, in asymptotes, by exhibiting a progression continued in any way whatever, we can show what will be. It might be thought that in this way men also will be able to reach certitude in the case of contingent truths. But we must reply that though there is indeed similitude, there is not complete agreement, and that there can be respects which, by an analysis continued in any way, would never reveal so much as is enough for certainty, and which are viewed perfectly only by him whose intellect is infinite. Just as in the case of asymptotes and incommensurables, so also in the case of contingent propositions we can perceive many things with certainty in accordance with exactly this principle, i. e., that

all truth must be provable; and consequently if all things on each of the two sides are in the hypotheses in the same mode, nothing can be different in the conclusions; and we can with certainty perceive other things of this sort, which are true in the case of necessary propositions just as in the case of contingent propositions, for they are reflexive. But we are not so capable of rendering the complete account of contingent propositions as we are of setting forth asymptotes perpetually and running over infinite progressions of numbers.

SUMMARY OF LEIBNIZ'S HOPES FOR THE FRUITFULNESS OF THIS DISCOVERY (29 verso, sec. 137)

(137) Therefore we have revealed many   [29 verso] secrets of great significance for the analysis of all our cogitations, and for the discovery and demonstration of truths. Perhaps in this way all truths could be explained by numbers: how contingent truths may arise, and how it is that to an extent they have the nature of incommensurable numbers; how absolute and hypothetical truths have one and the same laws, and are covered by the same general theorems, with the result that all syllogisms become categorical; and finally what is the origin of abstracts. This last matter it will be worthwhile to explain distinctly now very shortly.

ABSTRACTION (29 verso, sec. 138-sec. 143)

(138) If the proposition "A is B" is considered as a term, as we have explained can be the case, then an abstraction arises, namely, the A is B; and if from the proposition "A is B" there follows the proposition "C is D," then from it the following new proposition is made: "The A is B is or contains the C is D," or "The B-ness of A contains the D-ness of C," or "The B-ness of A is the D-ness of C."

(139) In general, however, if it is said that something is B, then this itself, i. e., that something is B. is nothing other than B-ness itself; thus the something is an animal is nothing other than animality. But the man is an animal is animality of man. From this we have knowledge of the origin of abstraction as well as of such an obliquity.

(140) But is the abstraction of "Every man is an animal" expressed by such an abstraction? Or by this: "Animality of each man"? This in any case is very much different from "all animality of man." If only some man is learned, "all learning of a man" is a true' term; but unless every man be learned "the erudition of all men" is a false term. That is, unless someone understands the term inclusively, as sometimes in geometry when under all motion is subsumed that whose speed is infinitely small or which is at rest. It seems also that "the erudition of every man" can be expressed as "the erudition of humanity." But I should rather not do this, if we follow what was said above, because "humanity of some" is nothing else than the abstraction something-is-a-man.

(140a) Or, since from the fact that some man is learned, it follows: "Some learned thing is a man," is it going to be permissible to say: "the learning of a man" is "the humanity of the learned"? I think so.

*39

(142) But how with an abstraction may we produce negative propositions, for example, "Some man is not learned"? Of course, as the negation of "man" is "non-humanity," so the negation of "the learning of a man" is "the non-learning of a man." And if it be said "No man is a stone," the abstract of it or the no-man-is-a-stone-ness will have to be expressed as "non-stone-ness of every man." Or will it be permissible to say "the stoneness of no man" or "stoneness of non-man"? I think not; and certainly this does not express that no man is a stone.

---

*39 (141) How shall we explain quantity in abstractions, for example, when A is twice as hot as B, or when the heat of A is twice the heat of B? Of course, that A is hot is the heat of A. Thus if the fact that A is hot be to the fact that B is hot as 2 is to 1, the heat of A will be twice the heat of B. But we must see further how the fact that A is hot can be to the fact that B is hot as one number to another number. This comes about because the cause which brings it about by uniform action that A is hot will also bring it about, by a continuation of such action once more, that B is hot; the sign by which we know that something is hot is a continuum and in one is twice what it is in the other. But much circumspection is necessary here; thus although thermometers are signs of the degrees of heat, they are not to be divided equally.

(143) Moreover, we ought to see whether this doctrine agrees with the predications of abstractions. "Greenness is a color" is a good predication. Why is this so? Or because a thing is green does it follow that the same thing is colored? But let us see whether or not there are examples to the contrary. "A circle is uniform; the same circle is plane." Notwithstanding it cannot be said that uniformity is planeness because planeness does not follow from uniformity. Or shall we say "The uniformity of the circle is the planeness"? Indeed it seems that from the proposition "The circle is uniform" "The circle is plane" follows. Of course, the truth is that it does not follow from this proposition any more than from any other proposition about the circle. Consequently, we ought to see whether the predications of abstractions seem to postulate not only this consequent but also something further. How is it that, because each circle is uniform, or because, if A is a circle, it follows that A is uniform, it is permissible in fact to say "Circularity is uniformity"? Thus it will be permissible to say with equal authority "Circularity is planeness." Then it will be possible to say "Something which is uniformity is planeness." Nevertheless I am still somewhat perplexed in these matters. In fact, if uniformity is the same as the uniform, and planeness as the plane, or it is true at any time that the fact that A is uniform involves the fact that A is plane, it will be possible to say "Uniformity in respect of a center is planeness or existence in a plane." And just as in concretes there are predications *per accidens*, as when the musician is a poet, I do not see why they are not also admitted in abstractions, as for example that some uniformity is planeness. Therefore we shall say correctly that the uniformity of the circle is planeness, and so we shall be able to follow a general rule. But how are we to unite these in circularity? There is a question whether, because we say "Circularity is uniformity, and circularity is planeness," it will be permissible to say "Uniformity is circularity-planeness." Also, there is a question whether or not the functions of categories seem to be mixed so that one can say that some quality is a quantity. There is quantity whenever from the fact that anything is of a certain kind it follows that there is so much of it. And so? Provided that it could not be said that every quality is a

quantity. There is a question whether in the case of such a universal proposition in the abstract necessity follows in the concrete; I think not, for there are contingent connections which are always true but which depend upon [free] actions.

ESSENTIAL AND EXISTENTIAL PROPOSITIONS OF SECOND AND THIRD ADJECTION (30 recto, sec. 144-sec. 151)

(144) Propositions are either essential or   [30 recto] existential; and both are either of a second or of a third adjection. *An essential proposition of a third adjection* is, for example, "A circle is a plane figure." *An essential proposition of a second adjection* is, for example, "A figure related in the same way to some one point is plane"; "is," I say, *i. e.,* can be understood, can be conceived. Among various figures there is some one which has this nature also, just as if I were to say "A plane figure related in the same way to some one point is a being or thing." *An existential proposition of a third adjection*: "Every man is or exists liable to sin"; this of course is an existential or contingent proposition. *An existential proposition of a second adjection*: "Man liable to sin is or exists, or is actually a being."

(145) From every proposition of third adjection a proposition of second adjection can be made, if the predicate is compounded with the subject into one term, and this is declared to be or to exist, *i. e.,* it is said that the thing is, either in any way whatever or actually existing.

(146) A particular affirmative proposition "Some A is B" transformed into a proposition of the second adjection will be like this: "AB is," *i. e.,* "AB is a thing"—either possible or actual, according as the proposition is essential or existential.

(147) A universal affirmative proposition is not as easily transformed—in this manner at any rate—into a proposition of the second adjection, for from "All A is B" it is not permissible without further ado to form "All AB is." When AB is the same as BA, it is equally permissible to say "All BA is" and "All B is A." So one will have to say "All A containing B is." We shall soon make it evident by another account how a universal affirmative proposition is reduced to a proposition of the second adjection.

(148) A particular negative proposition "Some A is not B" will be transformed into a proposition of the second adjection in this way: "A-non-B is," *i. e.*, A which is not B is a certain thing, possible or actual, according as the proposition is essential or existential.

(149) A universal negative proposition is transformed into a proposition of the second adjection by the negation of a particular affirmative proposition. For example, "No A is B," *i. e.*, "AB is not," or "AB is not a thing." Also, it may be expressed in this way: "No A is B," *i. e.*, "All A containing non-B is."

(150) The universal affirmative proposition is transformed into a proposition of the second adjection by the negation of a particular negative proposition with the result that "All A is B" is the same as "A-non-B is not" or "_____ is not a thing," or even (as I have said in number 147) "A containing B is a thing." However what follows, as I have already said, is not as pertinent, even if it be true, because it is superfluous, for B is already contained in A. But if not every A is a B, a new thing is made from AB.

(151) Therefore we have propositions of the third adjection reduced in this way to propositions of the second adjection:

"Some A is B" gives *"AB is a thing."*
"Some A is not B" gives *"A-non-B is a thing."*
"All A is B" gives *"A-non-B is not a thing."*
"No A is B" gives *"AB is not a thing."*

REPRESENTATION OF A, E, I, AND O PROPOSITIONS BY THE EQUALITY OR INEQUALITY OF CONCEPTS TO THEMSELVES
(30 recto, sec. 152-sec. 154)

(152) Since it is possible in the case of real concepts to rely upon identical propositions only to the extent that no supposed truth can be asserted without fear of its opposite being true unless it be ascertained concerning the reality of just the concepts—at least, the essential reality, though not the existential reality—it will be permissible for that reason to express the four species of categorical propositions in this way also: *The particular affirmative proposition*: AB = AB

(or AB and AB coincide, *i. e.*, AB is a thing). *The particular negative proposition*: A-non-B = A-non-B (or A-non-B is a thing). *The universal affirmative proposition*: A-non-B ≠ A-non-B (or A-non-B is not a thing). *The universal negative proposition*: AB ≠ AB (or AB is not a thing).

(153) Furthermore this presupposes that every proposition which has as a constituent a term which is not a thing is denied. So it remains the case that every proposition is either true or false, and furthermore that every one is false in which there is lacking a constancy in the subject or a real term. However, this is somewhat remote from our use of existential propositions in speaking. But this is not a matter which concerns me, because I am seeking fitting signs, and I do not plan to apply traditional terms to these propositions.

(154) But if anyone prefers to set forth the signs so that AB = AB, or AB is a thing or not a thing, and so that in the case where AB is not a thing B and non-B may coincide, namely, through the impossible, I offer no opposition. And so a distinction must be made between the term and the thing or the being.

First Formulation of Principles for a Calculus; Deductions from Them (30 verso, sec. 155-sec. 183)

(155) Therefore perhaps it will be better   [30 verso] at any cost to say that A = A can always be asserted symbolically, though when A is not a thing nothing is easily concluded from it. Thus if AB be a thing, it will be possible to form YA = ZB from it, for there can be formed from it: AB = R, and AB = RB; if there be B = Y and R = Z, YA = ZB is formed. On the other hand, if YA = ZB, then YAB = ZB. A = R and B = (R) already (or A and B are things); therefore YAB = Z(R); consequently AB= ((R)).

(156) A = A.   A ≠ non-A.   AA = A.

(157) A = B is a reciprocal universal affirmative proposition, which is the simplest. It coincides with non-A = non-B; and if it be denied one will be able to say "A ≠ B."

(158) D = ZC is a universal affirmative proposition.

(159) YA = ZC is a particular affirmative proposition.

(160) D = non-E is a universal negative proposition.

(161) XE = non-F is a particular negative proposition.

(162) There remain the terms in which non-YA is a constituent, *i. e.*, not such an A (or some A is not) which differs from not some A. Perhaps another formulation is to say that it is false that some A is B. Another is to say that it is false that such an A is B. Since some ambiguity arises here, it will be preferable to eliminate completely the Y letters, and then the following propositions will result:

(163) A = B, and likewise non-A = non-B. This is the simplest formulation.

(164) A = AB; *universal affirmative proposition.*

(165) AB = AB, if it is posited that AB is a thing; *particular affirmative proposition*, or YA = ZB.

(166) A = A-non-B; *universal negative proposition.*

(167) A-non-B = A-non-B, if it is posited that A-non-B is a *thing; particular negative proposition.*

(168) If A ≠ B, then either A-non-B will be a thing, or B-non-A will be a thing.

(169) "AB is a thing" is equivalent to "Some A is B," or "Some B is A."

"A-non-B is a thing" is equivalent to "Some A is not B" or "Some A is non-B."

"A-non-B is not a thing" is equivalent to a universal affirmative proposition "All A is B."

"AB is not a thing" is equivalent to a universal negative proposition "No A is B" or "No B is A."

(170) Meanwhile however it is important to distinguish the proposition "Some A is B" from the proposition "Some B is A," and similarly "No A is B" from the proposition "No B is A."

(171) The principles are:

First: A = A.

Second: non-A = non-A.

Third: AA = A.

Fourth: non-non = the omission of "non" itself, as non-non-A = A.

Fifth: if A = B, there will be AC = BC.

Sixth: if A = B, there will be non-A = non-B.

Seventh: if A = B, there will not be A = non-B.

Eighth: A-non-A is not a thing.

(172) If A = B, there will be AB = B.

Now A = B by hypothesis, therefore AB = BB by the fifth principle, *i. e.*, by principle 3 AB = B.

(174) If non-A = B, there will be non-B = A.

Now if there be non-A = B by hypothesis, there will be non-non-A = non-B by the sixth principle. Now non-non-A = A by principle 4. Therefore A = non-B.

(175) If A = non-B, there will not be A = B.

Now if A = non-B by hypothesis, there will not be A = non-non-B by principle 7. Therefore by principle 4 there will not be A = B.

(176) If A = BC, there will be A = AC. Now if A = BC (by hypothesis), there will be A = ABC = BCBC = BCC = AC.

(177) If A = YC, there will be A = AC, as before.

(178) If A = YC, there will be ZA = VC.

Now A = YC by hypothesis, therefore ZA = ZYC; if ZY = V, it becomes ZA = VC.

(179) If A = YC, there will be VC = ZA. This is evident from the preceding.

(180) If A = non-AC, there will be A = non-C (namely, if A is a thing). This must be strictly demonstrated.

(181) Non-AC = Y-non-C (= Z-non-Z).　⎫ These

(182) If Y-non-C = Z-non-A, it will be =　⎬ must be

non-AC.　⎪ demon-

(183) Non-A-non-C = Y-non-AC.　⎭ strated.

The Nature of the Proposition; the Proper Use of Indications of Negation (31 recto, sec. 184-sec. 186)

(184) Every proposition as it is ordinarily　[31 recto] expressed comes back to the fact that it says which term contains which, and the containing term, either absolute or with an addition, is inspected, and is said to contain an absolute content.

(185) "Not all" and "not some" ought not properly to occur in propositions, for these deny as much of a proposition as is affected by the sign "all" or "some," but they do not form a new sign "not-all" or "not-some"; so if I say "non- 'some man is an animal'," it is the same as saying that it is false that some man is an animal.

(186) "Some man is not a stone" means "Some man is

non-stone." The proposition "Every man is not a stone" seems to mean "Every man is non-stone." So generally we shall be interpreted in this way: *non* before *est* is interpreted as if the predicate were negative. But if the *non* precedes the sign, we understand that the proposition is denied.

SECOND FORMULATION OF PRINCIPLES FOR A CALCULUS; DEDUCTIONS FROM THEM (32 recto, sec. 187-sec. 191)

(187) I have already asserted above that those things which pertain to propositions can be explained and reduced as it were to numbers so that we conceive a term or concept in the form of a fraction, for example "ab-non-l-non-$m = H$" which means that H contains a and b, but the same H contains a and b, but the same H contains non-l and non-m; it need only be observed that aa is the same as a, and non-a-non-a is the same as non-a, and non-non-a is the same as a, and that the same term never contains at the same time a and non-a, or that a term which contains a is not said to contain non-a or the contrary. What contains ab contains also a, and what contains non-a contains also non-al.

(189) Therefore these are the principles:

First: $aa = a$ (from which it is evident also that non-b = non-b, if we posit non-$b = a$).

Second: non-non-$a = a$.

Third: The same term does not contain a and non-a; for if one is true, the other is false, or at least just such a term is not called true, but false.

Fourth: That A contains l is the same as that $A = xl$.

Fifth: non-a contains non-ab, or if l contains a, non-a will contain non-l.

Sixth: Whatever things are said concerning a term containing a term can also be said concerning a proposition from which there follows another proposition.

Seventh: Whatever cannot be demonstrated from these principles does not follow by virtue of the form.

(190) *The universal affirmative proposition* "All A is B" is the same as that A contains L or $A = XL$.

The particular affirmative proposition "Some A is L" is

the same as that A taken with something added contains L; for example, that AB contains L, if it is posited that B = LX, or that AN contains L, if it is posited that L = MN, and A = BM, for thus is formed AN = BMN = BL. So also "Some A is L" is the same as "AL contains L," or AL = AL; namely, if it is posited that AL is a thing or a term which is true, which does not imply its opposite such as "X-non-X."

The universal negative proposition: "All A is non-B" or "A contains non-B" or A = X-non-B.

The particular negative proposition: "Some A is non-L" or "AX contains non-L," or "AX = Z-non-L or even "A-non-L contains non-L," or "A-non-L = A-non-L," if it is posited that A-non-L is a true term which does not imply its opposite.

(191) If a universal affirmative proposition is true, the particular affirmative proposition is also true, or if A contains B, some A also contains B. Now A = XB by principle 4. Therefore ZA = ZXB (from the nature of coincidents). And if it is assumed (arbitrarily) that ZX = V, ZA = VB will result.

THIRD FORMULATION OF PRINCIPLES FOR A CALCULUS; DEDUCTIONS FROM THEM (31 verso, sec. 192-*[42])

(192) In true terms a universal affirmative   [31 verso] proposition and its particular negative cannot be true at the same time. If there were A = XL and VA = Z-non-L, there would result AVA or VA = AZ-non-L = XLZ-non-L, which is a false term.

(193) These same propositions cannot be false at the same time. If there be A ≠ AL, and A-non-L ≠ A-non-L, A-non-L will be a false term, therefore A = AL.

(194) A false term is one which contains opposites, or A-non-A. A true term is non-false.

(195) A proposition is what proclaims which term is contained or is not contained in another. Hence also a proposition can affirm that some term is false, if is says that Y-non-Y is contained in it; and true if it denies this. Also a proposition is what says whether one thing coincides with the other or does not coincide, for those things which coincide are mutually contained in one another.

(196) A proposition is false which contains opposites, as ⊙ and non- ⊙ .

(197) A proposition itself can be conceived in the form of a term; thus, that some A is B, or that AB is a true term, is a term, namely, "AB true." Thus that all A is B, or that A-non-B is false, or "A-non-B false," is a true term. Thus, that no A is B, or that AB is false, is a new term.

(198) Principles:

1st: Coincidents can be substituted for one another.

2nd: AA = A.

3rd: non-non-A = A.

4th: A false or non-true term is one which contains "A-non-A"; a true term, one which does not contain them.

5th: A proposition is what adds to a term that it is true or false; for example, if A be a term and to it be added that A is true or A is not true, one usually simply says that A is, or A is not.

6th: The addition of "true" or "to be" results in no change, but that of "false" or "not to be" changes a thing into the opposite. Thus, if it is said that anything true or false is true, it remains true or false; but if something true or false is said to be false, false is made from true, and true from false.

7th: A proposition is made a term if "true" or "false" is added to the term; for example, if *A* be a term, and "*A is*" or "*A is true*" be a proposition, "*A true*," or that *A is true*, or that *A is*, will be a new term, from which in turn a proposition can be made.

8th: That a proposition follows from a proposition is nothing more than that the consequent is contained in the antecedent as one term in another term, and by this method we reduce consequents to propositions, and propositions to terms.

9th: That A contains *l* is the same as A = *xl*.
*40

---

*40All B is C.	B-non-C is not.
All A is B.	A-non-B is not.
All A is C.	A-non-C is not.

*41

(199) *The particular affirmative* proposition: "AB is." *The particular negative* proposition: "A-non-B is." If it is posited that A and B are, *the universal affirmative* proposition: "A-non-B is not." *The universal negative proposition*: "AB is not." Hence it is immediately evident that there are no more propositions to be given as far as their number is concerned, and which of them are opposites and conversions. Now the particular affirmative and the universal negative are opposed, also the particular negative and the universal affirmative. Further, it is evident in the proposition "AB is" or "AB is not" that each term is in the same mode, and therefore conversion takes place simply. One can add "Non-A-non-B is" or "Non-A-non-B is not," but it is nothing different from "LM is" or "LM is not," if it is posited that non-A is L and non-B is M. The universal affirmative or "A-non-B is not" is the same as "A contains B." That A does not contain B is the same as that A-non-B is true. Therefore that A contains B is the same as that A-non-B is not true.
*42

---

*41"But this consequent from pure negatives, although it is proper, is nevertheless not obvious, unless the matter is reduced to affirmatives. From this it is apparent that this reduction of universals to negatives is not quite natural. Just as if A contains B and B contains C, A also contains C, so if A excludes non-B, then it includes B, and if B excludes non-C, then B includes C, and so then A includes C. If we assert "AB is" and "A-non-B is" as particulars, and "A contains B" or "A contains non-B" as universals, we shall be able to do without negative propositions. Indeed the negative does not affect the copula except when it is said that a proposition is false; otherwise it affects the predicate.

*42(200) If I say "AB is not," it is the same as if I say "A contains non-B" or "B contains non-A" or "A and B are inconsistent." Similarly if I say "A-non-B is not," it is the same as if I say "A contains non-non-B" or "A contains B," and similarly "Non-B contains non-A." Therefore in these few considerations are contained the fundamentals of form.

Commentary and Notes on the Text

THE manuscript is classified in the Bodemann catalogue as Phil., VII, C, 20-31 (24 pp. in folio) and appears in *OF*, pp. 356-99. The title and marginal note *1 appear to have been added later (C.), but the precise chronology cannot be determined.

AN ANALYSIS OF THE ELEMENTS OF LANGUAGE (20 recto-20 verso)

Leibniz believes that in order to construct a logical calculus for a universal language it is necessary first of all to know which concepts are simple, how many of them there are, and into what kinds of relations with one another they enter so as to form other concepts. Moreover, he holds—at least initially—that these concepts and relations can be revealed by an analysis of a natural language—more specifically the Latin language as used in his own day. The basis for this procedure is two-fold: (i) Leibniz assumes that the grammatical structure of Latin and its logical structure are quite similar, and (ii) he believes that language is a fairly accurate mapping of reality.

In this and the two immediately following sections Leibniz is concerned primarily with this analysis.

In his opening statement Leibniz insists that abstractions be made subordinate to proper subjects, and not hypostasized.

Abstractions are substantives made from other substantives or adjectives, *E. g.*, humanity, beauty. Man is what has humanity; the beautiful is what has beauty. But in a rational language it should be seen whether it is possible to abstain from abstractions or not, or at least to what extent it is possible to abstain from them. Phil., VII, B, ii, 12, in *OF*, p. 243.

It is possible to do without abstractions in a philosophical language, and we shall check many things by constituting it this way at the very first. In fact, an abstraction goes off into infinity, and it is folded back upon itself. But it must be considered that it is not possible with great ease to do without abstractions in reasoning and handling of numbers. Thus it will suffice as a maxim to avoid them as far as possible. Indeed I believe for certain that they are avoidable entirely in a properly constituted *characteristica*. Thus in geometry and arithmetic we understand by the lines and numbers not abstractions, but the things along with them. For example, circular, golden, silver, wooden, number, i. e., many things, e. g., a square number, that is, so many things such that they can be arranged in a square. Phil., VII, C, 159, in *OF*, p. 435.

In the succeeding three paragraphs he stipulates that "every term is understood to be positive unless there is indication that it is privative," and that " 'positive' is the same as 'being' "; logical negation he interprets as mere privation.

Both these positions are abandoned in the course of the manuscript. If "term" and "being" are synonymous, then universal terms will have existential import and universal propositions will imply the existence of their subjects. "Let there be *A is B*, then A can be called something. . . ." Phil., VII, B, ii, 32, in *OF*, p. 252. However, Leibniz defines "impossible" by "contradictory" and "being" by "possible" or "noncontradictory." Thus, by distinguishing between possible and impossible terms, he shows that he does not always take "term" and "being" as synonymous, e. g., the second paragraph on p. 21 recto and the concluding sentence of sec. 154. See *LLL*, p. 349.

Furthermore, logical negation is not merely a matter of the absence of some factor; it involves denial. Leibniz gradually comes to see this and to distinguish between negation and privation. (See *34)

Leibniz's acceptance of "every term as complete, or substantive," (p. 28) is an exception to the position sometimes attributed to him. For example, G. H. R. Parkinson has maintained that, for Leibniz, the concept of a substance must be complete (*i. e.*, such that from it we can deduce all the predicates of the subject to which the concept is attributed), and conversely a complete concept is the concept of an individual substance. In support of this position he cites *Discourse on Metaphysics*, Sec. 8, and *OF*, p. 403, respectively. See G. H. R. Parkinson, *Logic and Reality in Leibniz's Metaphysics* (Oxford: The Clarendon Press, 1965), p. 125.

Yet the discussion of "the sword" involves a different viewpoint. "The sword" is a complete concept, and the addition of the oblique relation "of Euander" to it does not make it any more logically complete. However, neither of these logically complete terms (*i. e.*, "the sword" and "Euander") is a substance in the metaphysical sense, *i. e.*, a monad. Thus, there are complete concepts which do not represent individual substances. See Leroy E. Loemker, "Leibniz's Judgments of Fact," *Journal of the History of Ideas*, VII (1946), 402. Leibniz seems to maintain consistently that the concept of an individual (in the metaphysical sense) is always complete.

The division of terms into those which are integral and those which are partial creates the problem of finding a method by which partial terms can be made into integral terms, since Leibniz maintains "it will be useful . . . to see to it that the terms are integral." (p. 29) However, the proposal here does not enable him to accomplish this transformation. A sentence such as "Caesar is similar to Alexander" cannot be treated in the same way as a sentence such as "Caesar is bald" because the former is a relational statement while the latter is of the subject-predicate form, and the relation cannot be made the predicate of the subject without merely retreating and covering up the difficulty. See *LLL*, pp. 433-34; Gottfried Wilhelm Leibniz, *Fragmente zur Logik*, ausgewählt, übersetzt und erläutert von Franz Schmidt (Berlin: Akademie-Verlag, 1960), p. 510, n. 24.1.

Leibniz's discussion of integral and partial terms suggests the more traditional distinction between categorematic (*i. e.*, complete) and syncategorematic (*i. e.*, incomplete) terms, and later on in *14 he makes use of this distinction as part of a more precise explanation of what he means by "term."

Further analysis (pp. 29-32) makes it clear that the "small number of integrals" to be considered as primitives as well as the means by which derivative terms can be created are not easily established. The classification cannot be carried out as neatly as Leibniz had first thought because a natural language does not have the requisite rigor and unambiguousness.

P. 28, l. 8. Since Latin has no article Leibniz inserts the Greek article *to* before "A is B" to indicate that he is speaking of second intensions. To this extent, the *to* is used as quotation marks might be used today.

P. 28, l. 15. Here Leibniz is using letters from the lower end of the alphabet for general definitions and letters from the beginning of the alphabet for particular examples. It is not clear whether "non-A, non-B, non-C, *etc.*" represent attributes of "non-Y" or notions subsumed under "non-Y." Perhaps they represent both. Leibniz uses "Y" for several different functions in the course of the ms.

P. 28, last line. That is, he remains a man.

P. 29, l. 26. This is not a separate paragraph in the original ms.

P. 29, l. 31. Use of the Greek article *to*. See note to p. 28, l. 8.

P. 30, l. 1. A particle is a minor uninflected part of speech such as an indeclinable adverb, a preposition, an interjection, and especially a conjunction. It may also be a prefix or suffix. However, on the basis of Leibniz's examples, he seems to restrict particles to prepositions only.

P. 31, l. 16. Use of the Greek article *to*. See note to p. 28, l. 8.

P. 32, ll. 1-3. For example, from "A with B" and "A in B" can be formed "A within B."

Simple Primitive Terms (21 recto)

Since the analysis of the natural language does not proceed as Leibniz had hoped, he must now accept certain terms as primitives only provisionally. It is difficult to understand how Leibniz arrives at this list of simple primitive terms. There is obviously a good deal of confusion here.

He accepts "term" as a simple primitive term! (p. 32) His previous discussion of integral and partial terms involves terms as symbols, *viz.*, whether they can serve as the subject or predicate of a proposition without the addition of any other word or phrase. In commenting on "individual" Leibniz says he is "defining only terms which designate either any individual or a certain given nature, or some certain determinate individual." (p. 33)

Yet he goes on to accept "being," "existing," and "all those confused phenomena of the senses which we certainly perceive clearly, but which we cannot explain distinctly, neither define them through other concepts, nor designate them by words" as simple primitive terms also. (p. 33) This must be "term" in the sense of what is signified. "*Terms* are the signification of names *in recto*." *Phil.*, II, 470. See Raili Kauppi, *Über die Leibnizsche Logik*, Acta Philosophica Fennica, Fasc. XII (Helsinki: Societas Philosophica, 1960), pp. 262-63.

His use of "term" then is ambiguous, and Leibniz apparently recognizes this, for in marginal notes and later passages in the body of the text, he attempts to define the word more precisely.

Nor is it clear why "individual," "this," and "I" must all be simple primitive terms. If for any given instance one individual can be distinguished from another, cannot "I" be defined? If so, there is redundancy.

Leibniz's discussion of whether "all the concepts which contain matter of a certain quantity, or in which homogeneous things accord with one another" are simple primitive terms (p. 34) raises a point of fundamental disagreement between Leibniz and the followers of Descartes. The Cartesians had maintained that the two types of created substances, mind and body, were distinguished, respectively, by the activity of thinking and the passivity of being extended. Such concepts are *per se* (both clear and distinct) and not subject to further analysis. Leibniz raises the question of whether further analysis is not possible on the grounds that thinking involves reference to what is thought, extension involves more than merely continuity and existence. But he is unwilling to take a firm stand on these questions, and so he suggests that we "proceed rather than . . . remain stuck at the very beginning by a certain excessive scrupulousness." (p. 34)

Thus, while he recognizes some of the difficulties involved here, he thinks it preferable to proceed in the hope that further discussion will bring greater clarity.

However, Leibniz makes almost no use of these proposed simple primitive terms in the remainder of the ms., and from this point on there is little reference to natural language usage as his efforts are directed toward the construction of a logical calculus more precise and rigorous than any natural language. There is then a rather distinct shift from basically linguistic considerations to conceptualistic ones which results in almost exclusive concern with the development of the logical calculus, the formulation of rules for derivation, and various issues (logical, methodological, epistemological, metaphysical, and theological) which arise out of this effort, as well as a more predominant interest in propositions rather than terms alone.

P. 33, l. 18. The followers of Thomas Bradwardine (*c.* 1295-1349), an Oxford physicist, viewed the increase and decrease in qualities such as heat, light, and color as the "intension" and "remission" for forms. Leibniz's use of the term "intension" may well have been influenced by this so-called Merton School of physicists. See Armand A. Maurer, *Medieval Philosophy* (New York: Random House, 1962), pp. 256, 258-59.

P. 33, l. 24. The German terms "Prägung" and "Anschauung" used by Schmidt in his translation perhaps more adequately express the Latin. Imagination for Leibniz is the power of "imaging."

P. 33, ll. 25 *ff.* Analogously, a physicist defines colors in terms of wavelengths, but the color and the wavelength are not the same.

PARTIAL TERMS; THE RELATION OF COINCIDENCE; THE DEFINITION OF "TRUE" AND "FALSE"; AND THE RELATION OF CONTAINMENT (21 verso-24 recto, sec. 59)

Although this section begins as an explanation of partial terms (pp. 34-35), it quickly moves away from any such general explanation as the introduction of intersubstitutibility as a criterion for the relation "same as" leads Leibniz to other considerations.

"That A is the same as B signifies that one can be substituted for the other in any proposition whatsoever without destroying its truth." But this criterion is not restrictive enough. For example, suppose that "man" is the same as "rational animal." On Leibniz's criterion this would mean that each one can be substituted for the other in any proposition without changing the truth-value of that proposition. But suppose the proposition is: " 'Man' precedes 'mana' in an alphabetical listing." Obviously, "rational animal" cannot be substituted for "man" without making the statement false. A more rigorous criterion is needed so as to distinguish between use and mention as well as between object-language and meta-language. See Nicholas Rescher, "Leibniz's Interpretation of His Logical Calculi," *Journal of Symbolic Logic,* XIX (1954), 2, n. 6; *7.

Of course, sometimes the coincidence is not immediately evident, *e. g.,* "triangular" and "trilateral." In such cases an analysis must be carried out until it is established that such concepts are possible and that they are really the same. (p. 35) Thus, Leibniz distinguishes between two forms of identity: a formal identity such as A = A, and a virtual identity such as A = B in which A and B are different in form and yet actually the same. See Kauppi, p. 71.

On the basis of this criterion Leibniz proceeds to define "coincidence," "disparity," "subject," "predicate," "all," "some," "is," "truth," "falsity," and certain immediate logical relations such as superimplication. Much of this section is, as it were, an exercise in developing these definitions.

While not especially well organized and often repetitious, the section introduces several other notions which are also fundamental to the development of the remainder of the ms.

(a) The stipulation that a letter may stand either for an integral term or for an entire proposition (*5) is intended to enable Leibniz to handle both terms and propositions in the same logical calculus. As we should express it today, the logical calculus would be open to either interpretation. The next step is to show that syllogisms can be treated as propositions (and consequently as terms).

(b) In sec. 1 Leibniz distinguishes between direct propositions and reflexive propositions on the grounds that the latter are about propositions while the former are not. See Kauppi, p. 169. As Leibniz points out, such propositions must be ranked in a certain order. If not, as Russell has shown, paradoxes are inevitable, for we may be led to believe that propositions about truths are, as true, about themselves. Of course, they are really second-order truths ('A is B' is true.) about first-order truths (A is B.). See John Passmore, *A Hundred Years of Philosophy* (London: Duckworth, 1957), p. 225. But Leibniz both in this paragraph and elsewhere (*e. g.*, Phil., VII, B, ii, 7, in *OF*, p. 239) stipulates that a proposition coincides with its assertion, and this makes it impossible to achieve the needed order. See Kauppi, p. 169.

(c) Since contradictions would vitiate his logic, Leibniz defines possibility in terms of not containing a contradiction (sec. 2) and then insists that all terms must be understood as possible (*8).

(d) The interpretation of "A is B" in the first statement of ms. p. 22 verso shows that the copula "is" may indicate either inclusion or identity. On p. 35 in defining "subject" and "predicate" Leibniz shows that "A is B," *i. e.*, "A contains B," can be defined by "coincidence." In sec. 30 "coincidence" is defined by the use of the copula "is." Thus the calculus of containing and contained can be derived from the calculus of coincidents and *vice versa*. See Kauppi, p. 74; secs. 36, 37. The possibility of defining inclusion in terms of identity, and identity in terms of inclusion, is important to the attempt to show that terms, propositions, and syllogisms can be handled by the same logical calculus. This will be tried by interpreting a syllogism as asserting which proposition(s) contain(s) which, and a proposition as asserting which term(s) contain(s) which.

The closing statement of sec. 16 shows that identity is not restricted to equivalence since "all A" = "some B." See Heinz L. Matzat, *Untersuchungen über die metaphysischen Grundlagen der Leibnizschen Zeichenkunst*, Neue Deutsche Forschungen, Abteilung Philosophie (Berlin: 1938), p. 65.

(e) Leibniz realizes that his algebra of logic differs in a very important respect from a mathematical algebra. While in the latter "AA" is equivalent to "A^2," in the former "AA" is equivalent to merely "A," or, as it is expressed in sec. 16, "man man" is the same as "man," *i. e.*, they have the same intension from Leibniz's viewpoint. Another important feature is dealt with in *11, *viz.*, the terms are not understood as mutually exclusive.

(f) While Leibniz says that what contains a contradiction is impossible (*e. g.*, secs. 32a-34), he draws a distinction between the meaning of impossibility when applied to terms and when applied to propositions. Impossibility in the case of a categorematic incomplex concept (*i. e.*, a term) is simply non-being, whereas in the case of a complex concept (*i. e.*, a proposition) it is falsity. See *13, *14, *15. *Cf.* *9, secs. 55, 75.

Leibniz's position seems to be this: Given a proposition whose necessity is based upon the subject matter involved, its negation is necessarily false, *i. e.*, impossible. A proposition which contains a contradiction such as B-non-B is false, and this falsity is logical, *i. e.*, the proposition is impossible. But in the case of categorematic incomplex concepts (*i. e.*, terms) impossibility means that there is nothing satisfying such a term.

This constitutes a modal logic of possibility and impossibility when applied to categorematic incomplex concepts, and one of necessity, impossibility, and possibility when applied to complex concepts.

See also the discussion of sec. 151.

(g) In secs. 40 and 41 Leibniz asserts that all true propositions are reducible to the form of an explicit identity, although in the case of some propositions we may be unable to accomplish this reduction ourselves. Such "propositions of fact" must then be assumed like hypotheses since their analytic character cannot be established by us.

The distinction between truths of reason and truths of fact is set forth somewhat more explicitly in secs. 56 and 57. (The distinction also appears explicitly in the earlier essay *On Freedom* (*c.* 1679) (*PPL*, pp. 404-410) and implicitly in the even earlier work *A New Method for Learning and Teaching Jurisprudence* (*c.* 1667 with later revisions) (*PPL*, pp. 135-43 for selections from Part I).) While later sections (60 *ff.*, 130a, *etc.*) develop the distinction somewhat more fully, these sections set forth quite fundamental considerations.

To establish the truth of an incomplex or complex concept, we must analyze it until we come to a fundamental truth, or to a truth already established on the basis of a fundamental truth; or we must be able to show from the progression of the analysis or the relation between earlier analyses and the present one that a contradiction can not occur—even though the analysis itself not be actually carried out.

As we have already seen, in the case of truths of reason an analysis involves only a finite number of steps (and thus such truths can be established by us finite beings), while in the case of truths of fact an analysis involves an infinite number of steps. This consideration is what leads Leibniz to propose that we might be able to establish truths of fact not by an analysis itself but from the law of the progression of such an analysis or the similarity of such an analysis to other analyses—analogously to a law of the progression of an infinite series in mathematics. See sec. 65. While, as Leibniz himself says, "this is extremely noteworthy," he never shows how such a procedure can be executed.

His failure in this regard makes his requirement that "if it be demonstrated that [a concept] cannot in any way be shown by a continued analysis that it is true, then it is false" too demanding, and he has to struggle to come to grips with this problem in somewhat different terms.

P. 35, ll. 26 *ff.* See sec. 30.

P. 36, ll. 11 *ff.* See sec. 29.

P. 36, ll. 17 - p. 37, l. 8. Leibniz uses "*enuntiatio*" here, but uses "*propositio*" in *8, the fifth paragraph of sec. 4, and almost exclusively throughout the remainder of the ms. as if *enuntiationes* were explicated by *propositiones*.

P. 36, *6 and *7. The Latin "*assumtitius valor*" has been translated as "more explicit value," but the translation is uncertain since "*assumtitius*" is definable only with reference to the present context.

P. 37, ll. 1. The " ⊙ " is the symbol for a syllogism.

P. 37, l. 24. Leibniz uses the line above "some truth" much as the bracket is used today for grouping. The "Y" in "non-AY" approximates "some."

P. 37, l. 31. The reference "by 4" is to an erased section. These initial paragraphs have been erased and begun again. (C.)

P. 38, *9. "Incomplex" is not equivalent to "simple." A term is an incomplex; a proposition, a complex. This usage derives from the terminist logic of the fourteenth century. See *14.

P. 39, sec. 16. For the reference to Aristotle, see secs. 83, 132. (C.)

P. 39, *10. See sec. 83. (C.)

P. 40, sec. 19. A "formal proposition" is one by which we talk about the terms themselves. For example, one could say, "I can think of 'AC' more readily than 'ABD'." Thus, Leibniz does recognize a difference between use and mention of a term. However, he fails to execute this distinction carefully in the formulation of his logical calculus.

P. 40, sec. 24. The substitution of "AY" for "A" involves commitments regarding existential import which Leibniz seems not to notice, e. g., the differences between "All trespassers are prosecuted" and "Some trespassers are prosecuted."

P. 41, sec. 29. See notes to secs. 16 and 24.

P. 42, sec. 38. The Greek article *to* is used in connection with "is." See note to p. 28, l. 8.

P. 44, sec. 54. Leibniz is invoking here a precept of his *art d'inventer*. See sec. 88. (C.)

Necessary and Contingent Truths (24 recto, sec. 60-25 recto, sec. 70)

The doctrine of necessary and contingent truths plays a very important role in Leibniz's thinking. These sections illustrate Leibniz's attempt to compose a definitive statement of the nature of these two kinds of truths, and the distinction between them. Initially, Leibniz takes the position that necessary truths are those which can be reduced to identities or whose opposite (*i. e.*, logical contradiction) can be reduced to a contradiction. An impossible proposition (*i. e.*, necessarily false) is one which can be reduced to a contradiction, or whose opposite (*i. e.*, logical contradiction) can be reduced to an identity. (Sec. 60)

Possible truths are those which contain no logical contradiction. Contingent truths then are those whose reduction to an explicit identity involves an infinite number of steps. (Of course, only God can complete such an analysis.) A contingent falsehood, then, may be defined as a proposition whose truth cannot be demonstrated. But this is inadequate, for we also are unable to demonstrate conclusively that contingent truths are true because of the infinite analysis involved. (Sec. 61)

This raises the question of whether it is sufficient for demonstrating the truth of a proposition that it be shown that there is no implicit contradiction. If so, then every possible proposition is true. (This position is ultimately given up since not every possibility is actualized. See *22.)

Complex concepts (propositions) present more of a problem in establishing their possibility than do incomplex concepts (terms) because the former require more extensive analysis, *viz.*, analysis into fundamental, true propositions which are established by definitions. Yet the definitions also must be shown to be possible.

This leads Leibniz to propose an empirical criterion of possibility: Whatever exists or has existed is possible, and whatever is similar in some respect to whatever exists or has existed is possible in just that respect. (The second half of the criterion is needed because "two complete things never are similar," according to the Principle of the Identity of Indiscernibles.)

But this criterion is not entirely satisfactory. For one thing, it does not enable us to determine the possibility of something which does not now exist, has never existed, and is not similar to what does exist or has existed. For another, as an empirical criterion it represents the inadequacy of a purely rationalistic criterion.

Leibniz thus concludes sec. 61 by saying that "every analysis of complex terms [propositions according to Leibniz's earlier stipulation in *14] as well as of incomplex terms [terms] ends in axioms, terms conceived *per se*, and experiential propositions." But he is unable to arrive at a criterion or set of criteria for establishing their possibility.

In sec. 62, Leibniz reasserts that "every true proposition can be proved"—though, of course, not necessarily by us! See sec. 61 and *22.

If the analysis of experiential propositions is like that of other propositions, there must be *primitive* experiential propositions which are known *per se* or axioms. And this leads again to the question of whether the analysis of propositions and terms goes on without limit or whether it ends in *per se* concepts. Yet it may well be that there are no *per se* concepts or that their number is so limited as to be useless for present purposes. If so, "no proposition can be demonstrated perfectly by reason," and we must resort to experiential propositions to help establish the possibility of certain concepts. (Secs. 62-64)

Though he returns in secs. 65-66 to an idea put forth in sec. 56, Leibniz introduces an additional consideration, *viz.*, that a proposition may be considered as true if from the rule of the progression of its analysis "the difference between those things which ought to coincide is less than any given difference." This proposal is apparently inspired by analogy with the method of limits in the infinitesimal calculus. See sec. 74. Leibniz never shows how this proposal might be carried out in practice.

Again Leibniz returns to the consideration of those propositions whose opposite is impossible, *i. e.*, to necessary propositions, to note that even here experiential propositions must be brought into play in order to establish the mere possibility of the concepts involved in an analysis of even a finite number of steps. (Sec. 67)

But it is not enough to establish that particular concepts are possible; it must also be established that they are *compossible*, *i. e.*, that they are compatible with one another. This knowledge too rests upon experiential propositions. (Sec. 68)

Now a Cartesian might answer that we can be aware of this in the very act of comprehending a concept. Leibniz answers that a concept can be comprehended in one of two ways: (i) as involving nothing else, in which case the concept is established as possible, but the only propositions relating to it will be identities; or (ii) as involving something else, in which case the additional concepts must be extracted and we must resort to experience as a criterion of their possibility and compossibility, *e. g.*, they exist in the same subject. Thus for us to get beyond mere identities, experiential propositions must be brought into play. (Secs. 68-69)

However, God judges possibility without appealing to anything but his own understanding. (Sec. 70)

Pp. 45-46, sec. 61. This section was badly corrected later by Leibniz. (C.)

P. 46. ll. 8-10. See *15, *22.

P. 48, l. 33. What "ought never to arise" is a contradiction.

THE DEFINITION OF "EXISTING"; THE COMPLETE CONCEPT
(25 recto, sec. 71—25 verso, sec. 74)

Leibniz believes that the concept of an individual involves all the concepts which can ever be ascribed to that individual. Thus if we could completely analyze the concept of the Apostle Peter, we would know everything about him—whether he has denied, is denying, or will deny, and even whether he has existed, exists now, or is yet to exist. A concept of a particular individual then is complete, while the concept of an indeterminate individual such as "man" or an abstract concept such as "hotness" is not complete. Of course, the analysis of a complete concept involves an infinite number of steps and so we cannot actually carry it out, though perhaps we can so approximate a complete analysis that it is less than any given difference. There is again no suggestion how this might be done. (Secs. 71, 74)

Another way to distinguish concepts of individuals from other concepts is to note that the addition of concepts such as "some" to the former is entirely superfluous—or, for that matter, the addition of any other concept. As an example, Leibniz compares "some Alexander the Great" with "Alexander the Great." (Sec. 72,*23) Yet this example and that of Peter are somewhat puzzling. Strictly speaking, all the individuals in the universe are monads. Yet Peter and Alexander the Great are not single monads, respectively, but clusters of monads. This, in turn, raises the question of whether we know the concept of any single monad. If not, it is difficult to see what part these considerations could play in the development of Leibniz's logic, methodology, etc. If so, why does not Leibniz use them as his examples?

Leibniz now turns to the question of what it means to say that something exists. It has already been established that not everything which is possible exists. Thus, existence involves possibility plus something else. What is this something else? Why is it that some possibilities achieve existence and others do not?

Since all existents are equally possible, "existence" could be defined as "being in the highest degree possible." "Or, what amounts to the same thing, existence is what is acceptable to a perceptive and proficient one." This, of course, involves assuming that there is such a being or, as Leibniz later says, mind. Existence then comes down to the question of what is not displeasing to the most powerful mind which exists, if any minds do exist.

Now, "it is more pleasing to a mind that that happen which has a reason than that which does not have a reason." And the overarching consideration here is the actualization of as much diversity as is consistent with universal harmony. Thus, a given possibility may not be compossible with another possibility. But that possibility which is compatible with the most other possibilities achieves existence, since this set of possibilities constitutes the best of all possible worlds, and the most powerful mind always chooses for the best. (Sec. 73)

P. 50, sec. 71. The Latin of the final clause of this section is unclear. The present translation is an attempt to reconstruct Leibniz's meaning.

P. 50, ll. 30-31. Use of the Greek article *to* in connection with "existing." See note to p. 28, l. 8.

Pp. 51-52, sec. 74. See secs. 66, 134, 136 for other attempts to implement the notion of indefinite approximation from the infinitesimal calculus. (C.)

THE STATEMENT OF PROPOSITIONS IN THE FORM OF TERMS, AND OF HYPOTHETICAL PROPOSITIONS IN THE FORM OF CATEGORICAL PROPOSITIONS (25 verso, sec. 75)

This section constitutes a very concise statement of how Leibniz plans to extend his *characteristica universalis* to cover both propositions as well as terms, and hypothetical as well as categorical propositions. According to Leibniz, the concept of the subject of a proposition contains the concept of the predicate of the proposition, or, to put it more carefully, a proposition asserts which term contains which. (See sec. 184) By eliminating the copula of a proposition (which Leibniz usually thinks of as some form of the verb "to be") and joining the concept of the subject and that of the predicate into a compound concept, a proposition can be changed into a term, or, to use the terminology of *14, a categorematic complex concept can be turned into an incomplex one. By analogy, Leibniz looks upon the antecedent of a hypothetical proposition as containing its consequent. Since the relation of "containment" is fundamental to both hypothetical and categorical propositions, Leibniz believes the former can be treated like the latter.

There are varied attempts later in the ms. to implement this program.

See sec. 137 for a similar statement.

On the statement about the falsity of incomplex and complex terms, see *13, *14, *15.

P. 52, ll. 24-25. "Understood perfectly" should be taken as referring to the possibility of a complete analysis.

THE DEFINITION OF "WHOLE," "PART," "CONTINUUM," AND "NUMBER" (25 verso, sec. 76-*25)

While the definitions set forth in this section are not particularly suggestive, a very important question for Leibniz's metaphysics is raised: When does a collection of parts form a unity, "one real being"? However, no answer is suggested.

THE USE OF "Non" (26 recto, sec. 76a—27 recto, sec. 106)

This section is an exercise in certain immediate logical conversions, especially obversion, with negation interpreted as privation. (See sec. 80)

To avoid confusion, Leibniz stipulates that "non" ought to be put in proximity to the letter or formula which it modifies.

P. 53, 1. 21. The line above the "Y" in "Y = AX" does not appear in the ms.

P. 53, sec. 81. Thus, "Y" means "some," and "Y" means "any."

P. 53, sec. 82. Strictly speaking, a proposition of the form "All A is not B" is ambiguous unless the context determines the meaning. The proposition may mean that not every A is B or it may mean that not any A is B. Leibniz at this point takes it to mean the latter. See secs. 92, 112.

P. 54, 1. 22. "*N. B.*" appears in the margin of this phrase. See sec. 54. (C.)

Pp. 54-55, sec. 91. The consequence drawn in this section and that drawn by the use of this sec. in sec. 94 are false, since the two particulars cannot be true at the same time (by the rule of subcontraries). Nevertheless, the conclusion is true (by the rule of contradictories). (C.) Leibniz should have used the law of subcontrariety instead of the law of contrariety.

P. 55, sec. 94. See note to sec. 91.

P. 55, sec. 95. In the margin there is a sec. 96 which has been struck out: "No non-A" is the same as "A" by itself. (C.)

P. 56, sec. 102. This is also the definition used by Peirce and Schröder. *LLL*, p. 346, n. 2.

P. 56, sec. 104. The line above the second "$\overline{BC}$" does not appear in the ms.

A Schematic Representation of Propositions and Terms (27 recto, sec. 107—27 verso, sec. 111)

If Leibniz's logic is to be as fruitful as he hopes (*e. g.*, in sec. 75), it must be possible to arrange terms and propositions in such a way that the relations between (or among) terms and propositions are quite evident and amenable to manipulation by relatively simple rules.

The present scheme is one of several which Leibniz proposes, and consists in the use of lines above terms to indicate various logical qualities and quantities.

A line above a term might indicate whether the term is universal or particular (*i. e.*, distributed or undistributed), while a line above two terms might indicate whether the relation between them is affirmative or negative, or whether they coincide or not. This would constitute a proposition which could be regarded as a term in a proposition of the next higher level. (See sec. 109)

This yields schemata such as those in sec. 107. In the first schema the loci are:

    1 the quantity of A (despite Leibniz's statement that it may represent quantity or quality)
    2 the quality of AB
    3 the quantity of B
    4 the quantity of AB
    5 the quality of (AB)C
    6 the quantity of C

See Schmidt, p. 511, nn. 24.5, 24.6.

    In the second schema, the loci are:
    1 the quantity of C
    2 the quality of CD
    3 the quantity of D
    4 the quantity of E
    5 the quality of EF
    6 the quantity of F
    7 the quantity of B
    8 the quality of B(CD)
    9 the quantity of CD
   10 the quantity of A
   11 the quality of A[B(CD)]
   12 the quantity of B(CD)
   13 the quantity of A[B(CD)]
   14 the quality of {A[B(CD)]} {EF}
   15 the quantity of EF

But see *ibid.*, pp. 511-12, n. 24.6, for a different interpretation.

    Furthermore, even a single term can be regarded as a proposition if only a "placeholder" is added to it. For example, the term "man" can be turned into a proposition by adding "is this truth" to it, since the addition of the term "truth" to another term is no more than multiplying by the number one in arithmetic; it merely supplies a "place." (Sec. 108) This gives a schema such as that in *29. The loci are:

    1 the quantity of A
    2 the quality of AV, *i. e.*, "A is true"
    3 the quantity of V
    4 the quantity of V
    5 the quality of VV, *i. e.*, "the true is true"
    6 the quantity of V
    7 the quantity of B
    8 the quality of BV, *i. e.*, "B is true"

9 the quantity of V

. . .

25 the quantity of AV
26 the quality of (AV)(VV)
27 the quantity of VV

. . .

See *ibid.*, p. 512, n. 24.6.

The advantages of such a scheme in terms of brevity and rigor are lauded in sec. 110.

But the scheme is a complex one—so complex that it becomes obvious to Leibniz that not all the relations involved where several terms or propositions are under consideration will be evident. The scheme is therefore abandoned in the hope of finding a better one.

Then in sec. 110 Leibniz again introduces the consideration that some rule for an infinite analysis might be discovered. This presumably "will appear more clearly" as the ms. progresses, but it never does.

Pp. 57-58. sec. 108. The Greek article *to* is used in connection with "the phrase 'this being'," "the word 'truth'," and "The 'this truth'." See note to p. 28, l. 8. The " . " refers to the second schema in sec. 107.

P. 58, *29. The "V" is for "*Verum*" ("true").

P. 58, sec. 109. "*Enuntiationes*" is used for "proposition" in the final sentence.

THE NEGATION OF PROPOSITIONS (28 recto, sec. 112 *30)

The import of this discussion is that to deny a universal proposition it is sufficient to assert a particular proposition (its contradictory) rather than another universal proposition (its contrary), to deny a particular proposition it is both necessary and sufficient to assert a universal proposition (its contradictory), and to deny a universal proposition involves the denial of a particular proposition (its superimplicant).

P. 59 l. 31-p. 60, l. 1. See sec. 82.

A LINEAR REPRESENTATION OF A, E, I, AND O PROPOSITIONS (28 recto, sec. 113-sec. 123)

This scheme of representing terms and propositions by a line involves using a line to represent only one term. The

actual or imaginary extension of a line represents the scope
of a given term; the heavy portion of the line (or the portion
which consists of a double line) represents what is under consideration as far as that term is concerned, *i. e.*, the part included or excluded in relation to another term. This indicates
the minimal limits, or what cannot be taken away. The small
vertical lines which appear at the ends of certain lines indicate
maximal limits. (See *31) For example, the line representing
the term B in an A proposition must not be longer than the
line representing the term A, and *vice versa*. But in a representation of an I proposition there are no such limits; it is
only necessary that a portion of the line representing A coincide with a portion of the line representing B. The relation
between two or more terms is thus represented by the spatial
relations of the lines.

As Leibniz himself points out in sec. 115, these geometrical
representations of A, E, I, and O propositions would be better
understood if they were arranged so that the line representing one term, *e. g.*, A, fell upon the line representing the
other term, *e. g.*, B. But that cannot be done on a two-dimen-
sional medium, so the lines are placed one below the other.
Leibniz himself connects with perpendicular, dotted lines the
heavy portion of the line representing A with the line representing B or the imaginary extension of that line. The horizontal dotted lines may be looked upon as representing indeterminate meanings, *i. e.*, the possibility of adding to the
meaning of a term up to the indicated limit. This yields:

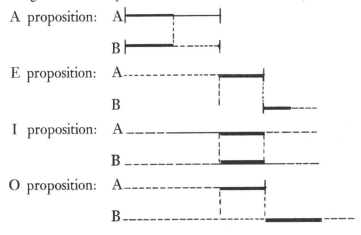

Apparently Leibniz prefers this scheme over a geometrical representation using circles because it clearly distinguishes the I proposition and the O proposition which are represented in the same manner by circles.

See Phil., VII, B, iv, 1-10, in *OF*, pp. 292-321, for other examples of these schemes of representation; *LLL*, pp. 25-31; Kauppi, pp. 177-78.

While one might expect Leibniz to adopt an extensional interpretation of terms and propositions when giving them a linear representation, he persists in his preference for an intensional interpretation. However, in secs. 122-23 Leibniz does recognize the possibility of an extensional interpretation, and even suggests how it would be done with a linear scheme.

This scheme too Leibniz finds unsatisfactory. Perhaps the major difficulty here is that the scheme becomes quite cumbersome when applied to several terms at once (such as in a syllogism) and so fails to make obvious all the logical relations which Leibniz wishes to indicate explicitly.

Pp. 60-61, secs. 116-19. These four propositions would be represented as follows:

$$AB = BY: \quad A$$
$$B$$

$$A = BY, \ A = BA: \quad A$$
$$B$$

$$BY = AY: \quad A$$
$$B$$

$$A = BY \text{ and } B = AY, \ A = B: \quad A$$
$$B$$

But see Schmidt, p. 512, n. 24.7. His statement of the first proposition is erroneous: $AB = AY$ [*sic*].

P. 61, sec. 123. The small vertical line at the right-hand end of the line representing A does not appear in the ms. However, it is necessary to indicate that the extension of A is not greater than that of B. The earlier representation to which reference is made is sec. 113.

A Numerical (Algebraic) Representation of Propositions (28 verso, sec. 124 - *38)

Leibniz now moves away from geometrical schemes and returns to a numerical scheme for representing terms and propositions like that developed earlier in a series of essays from April 1679. (Phil., 8, a, b, c, d, e, f, in *OF*, pp. 42-92; VI, B, ii, 14-15, in *OF*, pp. 245-47; 57-58, in *OF*, p. 258; VII, B, iv, 18, in *OF*, pp. 325-26. (C.))

The central notion of both these schemes is that if the subject-concept is viewed as containing the predicate-concept in a proposition, then when the proper numbers are assigned to these concepts the number(s) representing the subject-concept should be divisible by the number(s) representing the predicate-concept. Negative propositions can be looked upon as denying such divisibility. In the earlier scheme, Leibniz regards a proposition such as "A is B" as true if the number representing the concept A is divisible by the number representing the concept B., *e. g.*, if "animal" is represented by 7, and "man" by 21, then the universal affirmative proposition "Every man is an animal" is true since 21 is divisible by 7. In the present scheme, the numerical representation is algebraic rather than arithmetical. The universal affirmative proposition "(All) A is B" signifies that A (or the square or the cube of A) is divisible by B; while the particular affirmative proposition "Some A is B" signifies that AB is divisible by B. The particular negative proposition and the universal negative proposition deny that such divisibility is the case, respectively. (Secs. 124-27)

This algebra of logic is not strictly analogous to mathematical algebra. In the latter, AA is equivalent to A^2. But in the former a compound concept represented by the letters AA is equivalent to just A. For example, the concept "man man" is equivalent to the concept "man." The statement of a concept divided by itself is not admissible since division (*e. g.*, 1/A) represents negation (non-A) on this scheme. Thus, A/A would equal A x 1/A, where 1/A represents the negation of A. (Sec. 129) Implicit in this discussion is the condition that when division by B is attempted there must be no B as a "remainder": B must be eliminated. (Secs.

125 and 127 make this clear.) See also *LLL*, p. 344; Clarence Irving Lewis, *A Survey of Symbolic Logic* (Berkeley: 1918), pp. 11-12.

Moreover, Leibniz sees that negation and division are not the same. Division involves merely leaving out a certain part of a concept. For example, if the "rational" part of the concept "man" is left out of consideration the resulting concept is equivalent to the concept "brute." But negation involves denying that something is a part of the concept. For example, "non-rational" denies the quality rationality. Thus, "non-rational man" is an impossible concept because it denies of the concept "man" what that concept involves. This is why Leibniz says that division can yield nothing or non-being, but negation can yield impossibility. See Phil., VII, 232, n. **; Lewis, *Survey*, p. 377, n. 11.

Sec. 128 and *34 contain an alternate way of expressing terms and propositions algebraically using the sign of equality:

UA: A = AB (*i. e.*, "All A is B")

PA: AB = AB (*i. e.*, "Some A is B")

UN: A = A-non-B or A = A/B (*i. e.*, "All A is non-B," "No A is B")

PN: A-non-B = A-non-B or A/A/B (*i. e.*, "Some A is not B")

However, these schemes are beset with numerous, serious difficulties. For one thing, it is humanly impossible to assign the needed numbers, and even if this were possible there would remain the problem of how to deal with incommensurable fractions as a result of treating logical negation as division. This makes it clear to Leibniz that multiplication and division present formidable problems in formulating his logic. In the later logical writings of 1690 he shifts to the use of addition and subtraction.

The expression of particular propositions by setting a term as equal to itself creates another sort of problem because it involves denying the universality of the law of identity, *e. g.*, that one can always assert "A = A" or "A-non-B = A-non-B." (See *36, *37, *38)

P. 62, *33. See sec. 129. (C.)

P. 63, ll. 10-11. The final sentence is probably an allusion to the essays of April 1679 (Phil., V, 8, in *OF*, pp. 42-92). See sec. 187. (C.)

TRUE AND FALSE CONCEPTS: TRUE AND FALSE, POSSIBLE AND IMPOSSIBLE, NECESSARY AND CONTINGENT PROPOSITIONS (28 verso, sec. 130—29 recto, sec. 136)

While this discussion is quite similar to the earlier one concerning the analysis of propositions in secs. 56 *ff*. Leibniz does introduce two additional considerations.

(a) In sec. 130, he raises the question of whether a universal negative proposition asserts that something is impossible, *e. g.*, that no A is B, since it asserts something about concepts and not just about the actually existing individuals to which the concepts apply. But if so, it would follow that a given predicate-concept would be necessarily denied of the concept of any individual within the scope of the universal proposition. (Thus, Leibniz looks upon singular propositions as a special case of universal propositions.) Since, in the case of individuals, such a necessity cannot be demonstrated, Leibniz resorts to saying that, while what a true, universal negative proposition says is certain, it is not in fact necessary, because the requisite analysis cannot be accomplished. In *On Freedom* (*c.* 1679) this distinction had been used in an attempt to preserve a measure of human freedom by saying that something might be certain, but not necessary. See also the final sentence of sec. 143.

(b) At sec. 134, Leibniz returns to his notion that, while the analysis of a contingent, true proposition cannot actually be accomplished, something can be established from the nature of the analysis itself, and compares the difference between necessary and contingent propositions to that between intersecting and asymptotic lines or commensurable and incommensurable numbers. But he finally admits that such a procedure is not open to us because the analysis of contingent propositions is not like that of asymptotic lines or an infinite series of numbers. See sec. 74.

Pp. 64-65, sec. 131. See sec. 68.

P. 65, sec. 132. For the attribution of the intensional viewpoint to Aristotle, see sec. 16. (C.)

SUMMARY OF LEIBNIZ'S HOPES FOR THE FRUITFULNESS OF THIS DISCOVERY (29 verso, sec. 137)

Leibniz again expresses his belief that "many secrets for the analysis of all our cogitations, and for the discovery and demonstration of truths" have been revealed, and that much of his project can be completed. But his optimism is more guarded than in sec. 75.

His plan to treat all syllogisms as categorical rests upon the assumption that hypothetical and categorical propositions can be treated in the same way, and that disjunctive syllogisms may be treated like hypothetical syllogisms. See *Phil.*, V, 461, ll. 25-26; Karl Dürr, *Leibniz' Forschungen im Gebiet der Syllogistik*, Leibniz: zu seinem 300. Geburtstag, 1646-1946, hrsg. von E. Hochstetter, Lieferung 5 (Berlin: Walter de Gruyter & Co., 1949), p. 39.

P. 66, secs. 137 *ff.* What follows is from a different pen. (C.)

ABSTRACTION (29 verso, sec. 138—sec. 143)

At 20 recto, par. 1, Leibniz has written that he intends to treat only those abstractions which are logical or conceptual. In secs. 138-43 Leibniz attempts to explain how such abstractions arise.

In the initial two sections Leibniz seems to be suggesting something like the following: If it is proper to assert "(All) gems are hard," then it is also proper to "abstract" from this level (first intensions) and move to the next level (second intensions) where one can talk in terms of "the hardness of gems." Secondly, from "If (all) gems are hard, then (all) rubies are solid," we can move to the assertion "The hardness of gems involves the solidity of rubies." Thirdly, from the assertion that something is hard, we can move to the assertion that there is such a thing as hardness.

Leibniz believes that this helps explain how abstractions are created and also how oblique expressions arise (*i. e.,* "The hardness of gems" comes from "(All) gems are hard.") This is why, for certain purposes, we need not be so concerned about the distinction between the abstract and the concrete (*cf.* 20 recto, par. 1).

In secs. 140-40a and 142-43, Leibniz begins to investigate the question of which immediate inferences hold at this level of abstraction, and how negative propositions are related to the production of abstractions. Though not carefully developed, Leibniz does show how inversion and obversion can be carried out for some expressions.

The question of how abstractions can be quantitatively related is raised in *39 (sec. 141). Leibniz seems to have lost sight of the division of heat by degrees in this discussion despite his mention of it at the end of the paragraph. It is degrees of heat, not heat itself, that may be quantitatively related in this regard.

The omission of "free" at the close of sec. 143 is noteworthy. Did Leibniz perhaps see an incompatibility between his notions of freedom and contingent truth? See sec. 130.

Pp. 66-69, secs. 138-43. The Greek article *to* is used throughout these sections. See note to p. 28, l. 8.

P. 67, *39 (sec. 141). The final sentence refers to the fact that degrees of heat may not be exact linear functions of the expansion of mercury, alcohol, or whatever else is used in the column of the thermometer.

Pp. 68-69, sec. 143. "The circle is plane" does not follow from "The circle is uniform" any more than it does from any other proposition about the circle since "planeness" follows from "circle," not from "uniformity."

ESSENTIAL AND EXISTENTIAL PROPOSITIONS OF SECOND AND THIRD ADJECTION (30 recto, sec. 144–sec. 151)

Adjection is concerned with the combination of subject and predicate, and the position of the copula. The form of a third adjection is: subject-copula-predicate. The form of a second adjection is: subject modified by the predicate in a third adjection-copula. Since the copula can be either "is" or "exists," the adjection may be either "essential" or "existential," respectively (*i. e.*, the copula may or may not imply the existence of the subject).

Sec. 151 is important for its bearing upon the interpretation of Leibniz's modal logic. Nicholas Rescher takes "thing" (or "being," as Leibniz sometimes expresses himself) to represent logical necessity when applied to propositions. (See

Rescher, "Leibniz's Interpretation of His Logical Calculi," 10.) He bases this interpretation upon Leibniz's statement in sec. 32a that what contains B-non-B is impossible. (*Ibid.*, n. 43.) But he fails to take into account two of the marginal notes on this passage, *viz.*, *13 and *15. In these notes Leibniz says that the negation of a "materially necessary" proposition is either necessary or impossible, but that this does not hold for incomplexes (*i. e.*, terms) since impossibility in the case of incomplexes is "non-being," not "falsity" (as it is in the case of propositions).

Thus, Leibniz seems to take the following position: Given a proposition whose necessity is based upon the subject matter involved, its negation is necessarily false, *i. e.*, the proposition is impossible. But in the case of incomplexes (terms), impossibility means that there is nothing satisfying such a term. Thus, the addition of "thing" (or "being") to an incomplex concept merely asserts its possibility, not its necessity. (This follows from the interpretation of "non-being" in sec. 151 as a contradiction. See Kauppi, p. 181, n. 2.)

There is, then, in *General Investigations* a logic of necessity, impossibility, and possibility when propositions are under consideration, but of possibility and impossibility when terms are under consideration.

The relation of contingent propositions to this discussion is unclear, though perhaps Leibniz would regard them as contingent only because of our epistemological limitations.

It should also be noted that the mode of expression used in sec. 151 *et alii* involves allowing existential import for particular propositions and denying it for universal propositions.

P. 69, sec. 147. For the "other account" mentioned in the final sentence, see sec. 150.

REPRESENTATION OF A, E, I, AND O PROPOSITIONS BY THE EQUALITY OR INEQUALITY OF CONCEPTS TO THEMSELVES (30 recto, sec. 152—sec. 154)

It may be that this section is the source of marginal notes *34-*38 where the same scheme is found in a less developed form.

The scheme involves expressing the four traditional forms of propositions by asserting a concept as equal to itself if and only if there are things corresponding to such a concept, and to assert a concept as not equal to itself if and only if there are no such things. Thus, $A = A$ and $A \neq A$, respectively, affirm or deny the existence of something corresponding to A (A is a thing, A is not a thing). The universal affirmative proposition and the universal negative proposition are represented as the negatives of the particular negative proposition and the particular affirmative proposition, respectively.

This mode of expression is rather inconvenient, however, because it would require giving up the convention that "a thing is always equal to itself," and, as Leibniz himself notes in secs. 154-55, it seems that $A = A$ always is the case whether A exists or not.

See *LLL*, pp. 351-54.

First Formulation of Principles for a Calculus; Deductions from Them (30 verso, sec. 155—sec. 183)

Now for the first time in the course of the ms. Leibniz attempts to systematize the principles of a logical calculus which he has developed. This is impeded by the fact that there is no clear distinction between syntactical and semantical rules, the principles are neither entirely independent of one another nor adequate to the complete expression of the four types of propositions and the traditional relations between them, and the question of existential import, as usual, remains unsettled.

The principal scheme, developed in sec. 171, involves the use of letters as A, B, etc., the sign of equality, "non" as negation, and "thing" as an indication of logical possibility. But in sec. 177 Leibniz reintroduces "Y" as a sign of the indefinite.

He toys with the scheme and rather abruptly drops it.

P. 72, sec. 169. What follows is from another pen and in another ink. (C.)

P. 73, sec. 177. *Cf.* *10. (C.)

P. 73, sec. 178. "V" does not stand for "*Verum*" here and in sec. 179, but for the indefinite.

THE NATURE OF THE PROPOSITION; THE PROPER USE OF INDI-
CATIONS OF NEGATION (31 recto, sec. 184–sec. 186)

This section is something of an interjection to assert once
again Leibniz's conviction that containment is the fundamental relation of the proposition, and to warn against the
incorrect use of indications of negation.

The general rule formulated at the close of sec. 186 is
stated in terms of the language in which Leibniz is writing,
viz., Latin. In terms of this convention, "*A non est B*" means
"A is not B," while "*A est non B*" means "A is non-B" or
"No A is B."

SECOND FORMULATION OF PRINCIPLES FOR A CALCULUS; DEDUC-
TIONS FROM THEM (32 recto, sec. 187–sec. 191)

The second attempt to formulate the principles of a
logical calculus is marked *prima facie* by the predominant
use of small letters, a practice typical of the earlier work of
1679. Otherwise, it is quite similar to the first attempt. There
are the same failures to distinguish between syntactical and
semantical rules, to deal decisively and explicitly with the
problem of existential import, and to give an adequate basis
for all the derivations Leibniz attempts.

P. 74, sec. 187. The reference here is to secs. 124-29. (C.)

P. 74, sec. 189. Sec. 188 was left out by Leibniz.

P. 75, sec. 191. "V" here stands for the indefinite, not
"*Verum.*"

THIRD FORMULATION OF PRINCIPLES FOR A CALCULUS; DEDUC-
TIONS FROM THEM (31 verso, sec. 192-*42)

The third formulation of the principles for a logical calculus has the same fundamental defects as the other two
formulations. It is somewhat more concerned with semantical
problems, and introduces anew the question of how terms
can be changed into propositions and *vice versa*, although
now existential import is attributed to universal propositions
in the formulations in sec. 199.

While Leibniz claims that "in these few considerations

are contained the fundamentals of form" (*42 (sec. 200)) it is all too obvious that this is not the case.

P. 75, sec. 193. The sentence asserted is proved indirectly by showing that the sentence denying the identity, $A \neq AL$, contradicts the conclusion drawn from it, $A = AL$. See Schmidt, p. 513, n. 24.10.

Conclusion

From this detailed study of *General Investigations Concerning the Analysis of Concepts and Truths* several major conclusions have been drawn.

(a) Previous studies have been too restricted in their discussions of the work. They have tended to treat it in relation to only one area of Leibniz's thought, and thereby failed to see the work as a whole. These studies have usually focused almost entirely upon the logical content, and have attributed to these efforts a significance beyond what a more balanced judgment supports.

This study concludes that the major significance of *General Investigations* lies in Liebniz's attempts to relate his logic, methodology, epistemology, and metaphysics, and not just in the isolated logical or metaphysical doctrines contained in the treatise.

(b) While the earlier studies of Louis Couturat, Bertrand Russell, and, to a more limited degree, Raili Kauppi have suggested that Leibniz's metaphysics is either entailed by his logic or to a large extent derived from it, the present study maintains that at best there is a sort of analogy between certain of Leibniz's metaphysical doctrines and particular logical doctrines, and that the precise relation between these is quite vague. Of course, it may be these similarities were quite suggestive to Leibniz and thus that there is some psychological relation, but there is no clear evidence of an inferential relation.

(c) Claims for the significance of the logic developed in *General Investigations* have been, for the most part, too generous. While it is true that this statement of his logic is more wide-ranging, rigorous, and coherent than most other statements, it is not fundamentally different from much of Leibniz's earlier work.

(d) This is not, of course, to say that the logic developed in *General Investigations* is insignificant. (i) Although not completely satisfied with any of them, Leibniz did achieve several different modes of expressing the four traditional forms of the proposition. (ii) He saw that the copula "is" is capable of two interpretations, *viz.*, as containment and as identity. The seeming univocity of the compound concept containing its component concepts, the subject-concept of a proposition containing its predicate-concept, and the premises of an argument containing its conclusion led Leibniz to adopt too facile a view of the possibility of telescoping arguments into propositions and these in turn into concepts ultimately expressible as simple concepts and their connections with one another. While the interpretation of the subject-concept of a proposition as identical with the sum of all the predicate-concepts should have been suggestive in relation to his view of the concept of an individual as identical with the concepts of all that individual's attributes, Leibniz gives very little attention both to this interpretation of the copula and to the nature of the singular proposition, which has such concepts as its subject. (iii) He perceived the complementary relations between intensional and extensional interpretations of logical expressions, and indicated how his logic might be interpreted either way. (iv) His study of modalities led him to formulate a rudimentary modal logic of possibility and impossibility for terms, and another of possibility, impossibility, and necessity for propositions. (v) He was aware of the problem of existential import, although unable to deal with it decisively because of conflicting commitments. (vi) With the help of these and other insights Leibniz was able to make remarkable progress toward the formulation of part of what has come to be called "modern logic."

Yet what seems most to set the logic of *General Investigations* apart from Leibniz's other logical work is its status as the last major effort to overcome the problem of incommensurable fractions which resulted from using multiplication to represent logical composition, for when he resumed his logical activity some four years later, Leibniz resorted to using addition. *General Investigations* also seems to be the treatise in which Leibniz first saw that logical negation could not be treated as mere privation.

(e) The major inadequacy of the logic taken by itself is its inability to treat relations. While Leibniz recognized that certain propositions were not of the subject-predicate form, and thus could not be taken into account by the traditional logic of propositions and syllogisms, he never made the requisite supplementation; perhaps because he thought that such propositions were ultimately expressible in the subject-predicate form.

(f) The prime failure of the logic from the standpoint of the metaphysics is the former's inability to bridge the gap between possibility and existence. By logical analysis it can in principle be determined whether something is possible by showing that its concept is free of any contradiction. But given all possibilities, how is the more limited class of all compossible existents derived? How is the transition, or transformation, made from that atemporality and non-spatiality of the "region of ideas," God, to the temporality and spatiality of this actually existent world? There is no adequate answer in Leibniz, nor can there be one because his logic simply cannot deal with such.

(g) This is in part due to the basic methodological presupposition of the logic, *viz.*, that philosophical method consists in analysis and synthesis, which fails Leibniz at several key points. (i) Truths of fact cannot be established by such a method since their analysis involves an infinite number of steps, and we must ultimately resort to adopting such supposed truths as hypotheses and appealing to experience to justify them. Thus, truths of fact can never attain the necessity and universality of truths of reason. (ii) While the concept of an individual presumably contains the concepts of all his attributes, we are unable to derive any of them since again an infinite analysis is involved. Nor in synthesizing concepts do we have any indication of when we have reached a complete concept. (iii) We have to be assured not merely of the possibility of each component concept, but of its compossibility with all the other component concepts. Ultimately, this can only be established by us through asserting that what corresponds to each component concept co-exists with what corresponds to the others.

Thus what initially is stated as a method involving reason alone turns out to require appeal to the actual order of things, because the method of analysis and synthesis itself presupposes a means of ordering which Leibniz does not provide.

No doubt Leibniz himself saw some of these difficulties, and appreciated their importance. Indeed, it is in large measure as an attempt both to indicate and to overcome them that *General Investigations* must be understood.

Notes

INTRODUCTION

1. *OF*, p. 356, n. 1.

2. These correspond to the following division of the ms.: 20 recto-29 recto, sec. 136; 29 verso, sec. 137-30 verso, sec. 168; 30 verso, sec. 169-31 verso.

3. The Leibniz manuscripts had earlier been catalogued. See *Die Leibniz-Handschriften der Königlichen Öffentlichen Bibliothek zu Hannover*, beschrieben von Dr. Eduard Bodemann, Oberbibliothekar (Hanover: 1895). It is customary to use the Bodemann catalogue classification in reference when possible. Hereafter, Bodemann's classification of Leibniz's philosophical works will be denoted by "Phil."; his mathematical works, by "Math."

4. Gottfried Wilhelm von Leibniz, *Fragmente zur Logik*, ausgewählt, übersetzt, und erläutert von Franz Schmidt (Berlin: Akademie-Verlag, 1960), pp. 241-303, and 510-513.

————————, *Logical Papers*, trans. and ed. G. H. R. Parkinson (Oxford: Clarendon Press, 1966), pp. xxvi-xlix, 47-87.

5. *LLL*, p. 350.

6. *Ibid.*, pp. 354, 386.

7. *Ibid.* Couturat is referring to sec. 75 of the ms. Categorical propositions are usually expressed as declarative statements, *e. g.*, "All men are mortal." Hypothetical propositions are usually expressed as conditional statements, *e. g.*, "If all men are mortal, then Socrates will die." According to Leibniz, in a true, affirmative, categorical proposition the subject "contains" the predicate; in a true, affirmative, hypothetical proposition the antecedent ("If ....,") "contains" the consequent ("then . . .."). Therefore, the relation of "containment" can serve both. And this can be taken further: in a syllogism the premises can be regarded as "containing" the conclusion. An "incomplex concept" is a term, and a "complex concept" is a proposition. Leibniz believed that every term could be conceived in the form of a proposition, and that every proposition could be conceived in the form of a term, so there is an analogy here too. (See secs. 108-109.)

8. *LLL*, pp. 344-45.

9. *Ibid.*, p. x.

10. *Ibid.*, p. xii.

11. Bertrand Russell, *A Critical Exposition of the Philosophy of Leibniz*, new ed. (London: 1937), p. v. Since Russell's position depends to a large extent upon his untenable belief that Leibniz really had two philosophies—a "bad" one with which he entertained the court and placated

112

the clergy, and a "good" one which he kept to himself for the most part—attention will be given to the more careful position of Couturat. No doubt, Leibniz's philosophy does have an occasional character which leads Leibniz to express it in various vocabularies (scholastic, etc.), but there is no justification for holding that Leibniz had two philosophies.

12. Heinz L. Matzat, *Untersuchungen über die metaphysischen Grundlagen der Leibnizschen Zeichenkunst*, Neue Deutsche Forschungen, Band CCI, Abteilung Philosophie, Band XXIX (Berlin: 1938), esp. pp. 65-118.

13. *Ibid.*, p. 70.

14. *Ibid.*, p. 103.

15. The sentence is: "Das Denken oder die Vernunft, wie sie aus dem Gesamtdasein herausgenommen und zum Massstab des Seins gemacht wird, ist das allgemeine Vermögen schlechthin." *Ibid.*, p. 184.

16. Heinrich Scholz, Review of "Heinz L. Matzat, *Untersuchungen über die metaphysischen Grundlagen der Leibnizischen [sic] Zeichenkunst* . . .," *Deutsche Literaturzeitung*, Jahrgang LX, Heft 29 (16 Juli, 1939), cols. 1013-1016.

17. Heinrich Scholz, "Leibniz und die mathematische Grundlagenforschung," *Jahresbericht der deutschen Mathematiker-Vereinigung*, Band LII, Heft 3 (1942), pp. 238, 243. (The entire review is reprinted with corrections and additions in: *Mathesis Universalis: Abhandlungen zur Philosophie als strenger Wissenschaft*, hrsg. von Hans Hermes, Friedrich Kambartel, Joachim Ritter (Darmstadt, Germany: Wissenschaftliche Buchgesellschaft, 1961) as "Leibniz (1942)," pp. 128-51.)

18. Nicholas Rescher, "Leibniz's Interpretation of His Logical Calculi," *Journal of Symbolic Logic*, XIX (1954), 1-2.

19. From 1679.

20. Rescher grants that Leibniz himself was not always clear about the distinction between statements in the system (formulated in the object-language) and statements about the system (formulated in the meta-language). Rescher, "Leibniz's Interpretation of His Logical Calculi," 2, n. 5.

21. Rescher adds the qualifier "asserted" to repair the defect in Leibniz's statement of equality since it fails to distinguish between mention and use, and object-language and meta-language. *Ibid.*, n. 6.

22. *Ibid.*, 2-3.

23. *Ibid.*, 7.

24. *Ibid.* Rescher fails to explain what role the *General Investigations* played in the solution. In his article "Contingence in the Philosophy of Leibniz," *Philosophical Review*, LXI (1952), 26-39, Rescher argues that the principle of perfection is Leibniz's principle of contingence, and that this is a necessary supplement to the principle of sufficient reason and the principle of contradiction. But the principle of perfection is derived from the principle of sufficient reason.

25. Rescher, "Leibniz's Interpretation of His Logical Calculi," 7.

26. *Ibid.*, 8-9.

27. *Ibid.*, 10.

28. *Ibid.*, 11.

29. *Ibid.*, 10-11. It is quite evident from *General Investigations* that Leibniz already had firm convictions in 1686 about the role of "part," "whole," and "containment" in his logic. His position that in all true (universal, affirmative) propositions the subject-concept contains the predicate-concept makes this clear.

A part of the motivation for some of Leibniz's logical work in 1690 was the need to eliminate incommensurables.

30. *Ibid.*, 12-13.

31. Raili Kauppi, *Über die Leibnizsche Logik*, Acta Philosophica Fennica, Fasc. XII (Helsinki: Societas Philosophica, 1960).

32. *Ibid.*, p. 163.

33. Kauppi cites Leibniz's repeated considerations of the concept of truth as evidence for this position.

34. The actual reduction to identities applies only to necessary truths, but the possibility of reduction to identities in an infinite number of steps applies to contingent truths.

35. Kauppi, p. 164.

36. *Ibid.*, pp. 167, 170.

37. *Ibid.*

38. See secs. 47 *ff.*

39. The particular affirmative proposition is true if there is a Y which satisfies the equation; the universal negative proposition is true if the inequality holds for every Y. Kauppi, p. 177.

40. See secs. 83 *ff.*

41. See secs. 145 *ff.*

42. See sec. 152.

43. See sec. 155.

44. Kauppi, pp. 176-82.

45. *Ibid.*, p. 182.

46. *Ibid.*, pp. 66-71, 243-47, 164, 175, *et alii*.

47. G. H. R. Parkinson, *Logic and Reality in Leibniz's Metaphysics* (Oxford: Clarendon Press, 1965). In his later work *Logical Papers* (see footnote 4) Parkinson delineates Leibniz's various schemes for symbolizing the four traditional propositional forms (see pp. xxxvi-xlix), but as his treatment seems to be essentially the same as Kauppi it is not repeated here.

48. *E. g.*, secs. 16 and 132 of *General Investigations*.

49. *OF*, p. 53; *PPL*, p. 365. Parkinson also cites sec. 130 of *General Investigations*.

50. *Phil.*, VII, 211.

51. Parkinson, *Logic and Reality in Leibniz's Metaphysics*, pp. 17-22.

52. *Ibid.*, p. 55.

53. *Ibid.*, pp. 4, 182. On pp. 184-85, Parkinson gives a list of definitions, axioms, and theorems which he regards as the premises from which Leibniz's metaphysics can be derived.

54. See "Towards a Universal Characteristic," in *Phil.*, VII, 184-89, and *PPL*, pp. 339-46; *LLL*, p. 49.

55. Leibniz conceived of an *ars combinatoria* when he was eighteen years old, and in 1666 he published his *Dissertatio de arte combinatoria* (See *PPL*, pp. 117-33 for selections.). See "Préface à la Science Générale" (1677) in *OF*, pp. 153-57. Leibniz devoted considerable attention to permutations and combinations.

56. See *Phil.*, VI, ii, a, in *OF*, p. 156.

57. *LLL*, pp. 49-50. Leibniz considers grammatical analysis an indispensable prerequisite to logical analysis because there are certain inferences which cannot be handled by the syllogism (*e. g.*, David is the father of Solomon, therefore Solomon is the son of David), but which the universal characteristic must be able to handle. See *ibid.*, pp. 73-75.

58. Leibniz, *Selections*, ed. Philip P. Wiener (New York: Scribner's, 1951) p. 18 (trans. from *OF*, pp. 153-57).

59. Leibniz, *Selections*, p. 22. See *On Universal Synthesis and Analysis, Or The Art of Discovery and Judgment* in *PPL*, pp. 351-59.

60. This is also the title of the Port-Royal Logic which Leibniz certainly knew. See Antoine Arnauld, *The Art of Thinking: Port-Royal Logic*, trans. James Dickoff and Patricia James (Indianapolis: Bobbs-Merrill, 1964). The order of development of the logic in *General Investigations* approximates that of the first three of the four sections of the Port-Royal Logic: Conception, Judgment, Reasoning (*e. g.*, syllogisms), and Ordering (*e. g.*, analysis and synthesis).

61. *LLL*, pp. 176, 182.

62. *Ibid.*, p. 272.

63. Among this series of essays of 1679 are: *Elementa Characteristicae universalis* (Phil., V, 8, a; *OF*, pp. 42-49), *Elementa Calculi* (Phil., V, 8, b; *OF*, pp. 49-57); *Calculi universalis Elementa* (Phil., V, 8, c; *OF*, pp. 57-66); *Calculi universalis investigationes* (Phil., V, 8, d; *OF*, pp. 66-70); *Modus examinandi consequentias per Numeros* (Phil., V, 8, e; *OF*, pp. 70-77); *Regulae ex quibus de bonitate consequentiarum formisque et modis syllogismorum categoricum judicari potest per numeros* (Phil., V, 8, f; *OF*, pp. 77-84); *Calculus consequentiarum* and *Regulae quibus observatis de bonitate consequentiarum per numeros judicari potest* (Phil., V, 8, f; *OF*, pp. 84-92); and three fragments (Phil., VII, B, ii, 14-15, 57-58, and iv, 18; *OF*, pp. 245-47, 258, and 325-26, respectively).

64. $S = Py$ All S equals some P.   All S is P.
    $Sx = Py$ Some S equals some P.   Some S is P.
    $Sx \neq Py$ Some S does not equal some P.   No S is P.
    $S \neq Py$ All S does not equal some P.   Some S is not P.

65. *LLL*, pp. 326-29 *passim*.

66. *Ibid.*, pp. 329-35 *passim*.

67. *Specimen Calculi universalis* and *Ad Specimen calculi universalis addenda* (Phil., VII, B, ii, 16-17, 20-21; *OF*, pp. 245-47, 249). These essays are characterized by the use of small letters for terms and the absence of the sign of equality.

68. *LLL*, pp. 335-42 *passim*.

69. A fragment which Couturat dates at 1683 contains a sketch of an alternative calculus—the only one in which Leibniz tried to represent the *alternative* of several concepts by multiplication. See Math., I, 26, a, in *OF*, pp. 556-57; *LLL*, p. 343.

70. *E. g.*, *16; secs, 61, 68, 76a, 107, 151, 187; *42.

71. *Primaria Calculi Logici fundamenta* (Aug. 1, 1690), Phil., VII, B, ii, 3; *OF*, pp. 235-37; and *Fundamenta Calculi Logici* (Aug. 2, 1690), Phil., VII, C, 97; *OF*, pp. 421-23.

72. *Phil.*, VII, 211-17.

73. *LLL*, pp. 358-60.

74. Secs. 124 *ff.* in *General Investigations*.

75. The two most important of these fragments are found in *Phil.*, VII, 228-35 (No. XIX, *Non inelegans Specimen demonstrandi*) and 236-47 (No. XX). Again terms are represented by upper case letters and logical equality by a horizontal "8." *LLL*, p. 364, n. 3. In the first of these fragments Leibniz attempts a theory of logical subtraction, *e. g.*, $A - B = C$. Though not essential to the system and apparently given up by

Leibniz (since it does not appear in the second fragment), it is a noteworthy attempt to solve the problem of incommensurable fractions which arises in *General Investigations. LLL*, p. 376. (An English translation of these two fragments may be found in: Lewis, *A Survey of Symbolic Logic* (Berkeley: 1918), pp. 373-87.)

76. *PPL*, pp. 404-410, and 135-43 (selections from Part I), respectively.

77. Secs. 41, 56, 57, 60-66; *22; secs. 67-70, 74, 128, 130-37, 143.

78. Sec. 143.

79. Written in the winter of 1685-86, *Discourse on Metaphysics* represents an attempt by Leibniz to bring together his thinking on certain metaphysical and moral questions with far-reaching theological implications. See Leroy E. Loemker, "A Note on the Origin and Problem of Leibniz's Discourse of 1686," *Journal of the History of Ideas*, VIII (1947), 449; *PPL*, p. 464. For the text, see *ibid.*, pp. 465-506; *Phil.*, IV, 427-63. The tenor and organization of the work make it clear that it is related to Leibniz's project of an apologetic for generally accepted Christian doctrines as an aid in promoting church union. For a statement of the more specific position that *Discourse* is probably a preliminary study for the preface to Leibniz's projected *Catholic Demonstrations*, see Loemker, "A Note. . .," 449-52. While *General Investigations* is substantially different in content, emphasis, and purpose, it does have some topics in common with *Discourse*, most notably the distinction between two kinds of truth, and the nature of the concept of an individual.

There is no indication, Couturat's and Kauppi's claim notwithstanding, that *General Investigations* provides the logical foundations of *Discourse*. For example, the nature of the concept of an individual is treated in fundamentally the same way in the two treatises, yet never established on logical grounds, and the treatment of the distinction between two kinds of truth predates both works.

80. *Discourse on Metaphysics*, Sec. 13.

81. Gottfried Wilhelm Leibnitz [*sic*], *New Essays Concerning Human Understanding*, trans. Alfred Gideon Langley, 3rd ed. (LaSalle, Illinois: The Open Court Publishing Co., 1949), pp. 404, 410, 515-16 (Bk. IV, Ch. II, Sec. 1, and Ch. XI, Sec. 13).

82. Page 50 recto, par. 5.

83. See Leroy E. Loemker, "Leibniz's Judgments of Fact," *Journal of the History of Ideas*, VII (1946), 402.

84. "Complete" and "individual" are equivalent in Leibniz's discussion. In sec. 74 of *General Investigations* Leibniz indicates that the notion of an individual is complete. In an undated fragment, he says: "If a concept be complete, or such that from it a reason can be given for all the predicates of the subject to which this concept can be attributed it will be the concept of an individual substance, and the reverse." (Phil., VII, C, 63 verso, in *OF*, p. 402.)

85. Sec. 72, *23; Parkinson, *Logic and Reality in Leibniz's Metaphysics*, p. 127.

86. Leibniz ultimately resorts to an empirical criterion. "Sensitive knowledge. . . [is] that which establishes the existence of particular beings." *New Essays*, p. 419 (Bk. IV, Ch. II, Sec. 14). See also *General Investigations*, sec. 61.

87. Couturat's claim that Leibniz's metaphysics "rests uniquely upon the principles of his logic" is based upon his interpretation of an undated

and untitled manuscript which probably comes from the period 1680-84 and is usually called "First Truths" (in *OF*, pp. 518-23; *PPL*, pp. 411-17). (See "Sur la metaphysique de Leibniz," *Revue de metaphysique et de morale*, X (1902), 1-25.) Generally speaking, first truths are identities, and all other truths are reducible to them by means of definitions or an analysis of concepts. This means then that all truth can be proved *a priori*, independently of experience. Leibniz then proceeds to derive some of the principles of his metaphysics, beginning with the principle that, if the whole is greater than its parts, then the predicate always inheres in the subject—explicitly in the case of identities, implicitly otherwise (and this can be revealed by an analysis). It follows then that there is nothing without a reason, since otherwise there would be truths which could not be proved *a priori* or reduced to identities. Therefore, there are no two individual things in nature which differ only numerically, since it must be possible to give a reason why they are different and it must be some difference within themselves. By the introduction of additional definitions, Leibniz goes on to prove such principles as: "The complete or perfect concept of an individual involves all its predicates, past, present, and future"; "Every individual substance involves the whole universe in its perfect concept"; "No created substance exerts a metaphysical action or influence upon another"; and "There is no corporeal substance in which there is nothing but extension, or magnitude, figure, and their variations."

Couturat takes the derivation of these principles as evidence that Leibniz's metaphysics arises out of his logic. But what Couturat fails to see is that the definitions which Leibniz introduces and by means of which (together with the laws of identity and sufficient reason) the principles are derived are not themselves always identities and many of them are primarily metaphysical in character. (See Loemker, "Leibniz's Judgments of Fact," 398; *PPL*, p. 411.) Of course, if the principles which one introduces are already metaphysical in character, then one can derive certain metaphysical principles by the use of basic rules of logic such as the law of identity. But that does not in the least prove that the metaphysical principles are derived from the logical principles.

Thus, Couturat's claim is not supported by the evidence which he adduces, and Russell's position is thereby undermined since he too accepts "First Truths" as confirmation for his view. (See Russell, p. v.)

Matzat attempts to indicate the relation between Leibniz's logic and his metaphysics on different grounds. (See Matzat, pp. 70, 103.) What seems to commend Matzat's view that a proposition is fundamentally a symbolic means of representing the relation between ideas and God is Leibniz's belief that the simple concepts are grounded in the simple perfections of God, and that true propositions indicate the proper relations between (or among) concepts. But this means that God is the proper subject of all true propositions—a position which Leibniz would surely reject because of its monistic implications. Matzat's assertion that the relation between Leibniz's metaphysics and his logic is that monads are the most primitive from the standpoint of the natural representation of the universe in the soul, while the first elements of the logical calculus are the most primitive in terms of the artificial representation of the universe, indicates, not the relation between the two, but merely the respective status of each.

88. Sec. 184.

89. Perhaps Leibniz would restrict this to affirmative propositions (so that negative propositions have non-containment as the fundamental relation) and further to universal propositions (so that particular propositions must be viewed as asserting containment or non-containment only implicitly, *i.e.*, the concept of the subject and the concept of the predicate are not identical but do have some concept in common). The doctrine obviously must be restricted to true propositions.

90. The logical relations are quite different. For example, a singular proposition has a contradiction, but no opposite, while a universal proposition has both.

91. *E. g.*, *Phil.*, I, 14, c, 7 (in *OF*, p. 8); *Phil.*, VIII, 7 recto (in *OF*, p. 521, and *PPL*, pp. 413-414), "First Truths."

92. Parkinson, *Logic and Reality in Leibniz's Metaphysics*, p. 45.

93. *Phil.*, VII, 401.

94. "Letter to Des Bosses," *Phil.*, II, 486 (in *PPL*, p. 992).

95. Letter to Des Billettes, Dec. 4/14, 1696, in *Phil.*, VII, 451, and *PPL*, p. 771.

96. *LLL*, p. 438.

97. The fundamental relation between concepts in a proposition is that of containment. But this relation is obvious only to God where truths of fact are concerned. We must appeal to actually existent things to determine their truth. But God can judge concepts without having to appeal to anything but his own understanding.

98. See secs. 16 and 132 of *General Investigations* for Leibniz's noting of his agreement with Aristotle. See Lewis, *A Survey of Symbolic Logic*, p. 14, and Parkinson, *Logic and Reality in Leibniz's Metaphysics*, pp. 17-22 for other views on this question.

99. For replies to Couturat, see Rescher, "Leibniz's Interpretation of His Logical Calculi," 12-13; Lewis, *A Survey of Symbolic Logic*, p. 14; and Clarence Irving Lewis and Cooper Harold Langford, *Symbolic Logic* (New York: 1932), p. 7, n. 2.

100. Secs. 122, 123. Rescher's work shows that the logic developed in *General Investigations* is open to either interpretation. See "Leibniz's Interpretation of His Logical Calculi." Further, Carnap has established that for every known intensional language S_1 an extensional language S_2 can be constructed such that S_1 can be substituted into S_2. See Rudolf Carnap, *The Logical Syntax of Language* (New York: 1937), pp. 245-46.

101. See, for example, Heinrich Scholz, *Concise History of Logic*, trans. Kurt F. Leidecker (New York: Philosophical Library, 1961), p. 58.

However, Gottfried Martin disagrees with this assessment. "I find it hard to believe the allegation that Leibniz's work had no influence on the development of modern logic, and that his work only became known after modern logic had developed independently." Gottfried Martin, *Leibniz: Logic and Metaphysics*, trans. K. J. Northcott and P. G. Lucas (Manchester: Manchester Univ. Press, 1964), p. 92. Such an allegation Martin regards as all the more remarkable since in Martin's view Leibniz's published works such as the *New Essays* (1795) and the *Theodicy* (1840) contain many indications of Leibniz's aims in logic. Martin suggests that the question of historical connection is still an open one. *Ibid.*, p. 41. But the fact remains that none of the manuscripts in which Leibniz attempted to execute his aims was published (with the exception of the one in Erdmann [see below]) until after the groundwork of the algebra of logic in the nineteenth century was already laid.

It is unlikely that Boole knew anything of the details of Leibniz's logical work when he first conceived the idea of an algebra of logic. If he used Erdmann's edition of Leibniz (1840) he may have seen *Non Inelegans Specimen Demonstrandi in Abstractis,* which was the only important piece of Leibniz's work on symbolic, mathematical logic then generally available. Boole's *Mathematical Analysis of Logic* appeared in 1847, followed by *The Laws of Thought* in 1854. See William Kneale, "Boole and the Revival of Logic," *Mind,* LVII (1948), 158-59.

102. Innocentius Marie Bocheński, *A History of Formal Logic,* trans. and ed. Ivo Thomas (Notre Dame: Univ. of Notre Dame Press, 1961), pp. 258, 267, 269, 276; Lewis, *A Survey of Symbolic Logic,* pp. 3-6; Heinrich Scholz, "Leibniz und die mathematische Grundlagenforschung," 238.

103. See *PPL,* pp. 13, 548, n. 12.

104. See, *e. g.,* the discussion on page 20 recto.

Selected Bibliography

Bocheński, Innocentius Marie. *A History of Formal Logic*, trans. and ed. Ivo Thomas. Notre Dame: Univ. of Notre Dame Press, 1961.

Carnap, Rudolf. *The Logical Syntax of Language*. New York: Harcourt, Brace, 1937.

LLL Couturat, Louis. *La logique de Leibniz*. Paris: 1901.

———. "Sur la metaphysique de Leibniz." *Revue de metaphysique et de morale*, X (1902), 1-25.

Dürr, Karl. "Die mathematische Logik von Leibniz." *Studia philosophica*, VII (1947), 87-102.

———. *Leibniz' Forschungen im Gebiet der Syllogistik*. Leibniz: zu seinem 300. Geburtstag, 1646-1946, hrsg. von E. Hochstetter, Lieferung 5. Berlin: Walter de Gruyter & Co., 1949.

Kauppi, Raili. *Über die Leibnizsche Logik*. Acta Philosophica Fennica, Fasc. XII. Helsinki: Societas Philosophica, 1960.

Kneale, William. "Boole and the Revival of Logic." *Mind*, LVII, (1948), 149-75.

———, and Martha Kneale. *The Development of Logic*. Oxford: The Clarendon Press, 1962.

Phil. Leibniz, Gottfried Wilhelm. *Die philosophischen Schriften von Gottfried Wilhelm Leibniz*, hrsg. von C. I. Gerhardt. 7 vols. Berlin: 1875-80.

———. *Discourse on Metaphysics*, trans. Peter G. Lucas and Leslie Grint. Manchester: Manchester Univ. Press, 1953.

———. *Fragmente zur Logik*, ausgewählt, übersetzt und erläutert von Franz Schmidt. Berlin: Akademie-Verlag, 1960.

———. *Logical Papers*, trans. and ed. G. H. R. Parkinson. Oxford: Clarendon Press, 1966.

OF ———. *Opuscules et fragments inédits de Leibniz*, ed. Louis Couturat. Paris: 1903.

PPL ———. *Philosophical Papers and Letters*, selected, trans., and ed. by Leroy E. Loemker. 2 vols. Chicago: Univ. of Chicago Press, 1956.

———. *Selections*, ed. Philip P. Wiener. New York: Scribner's, 1951.

Lewis, Clarence Irving. *A Survey of Symbolic Logic*. Berkeley, 1918. (Reprinted, without Chapters IV and V, New York: Dover, 1960.)

120